CW00794118

THE CANINE THYROID EPIDEMIC

Answers You Need for Your Dog

W. Jean Dodds, DVM
Diana R. Laverdure

Wenatchee, Washington U.S.A.

The Canine Thyroid Epidemic
Answers You Need for Your Dog
W. Jean Dodds, DVM
Diana R. Laverdure

Dogwise Publishing
A Division of Direct Book Service, Inc.
403 South Mission Street, Wenatchee, Washington 98801
1-509-663-9115, 1-800-776-2665
www.dogwisepublishing.com / info@dogwisepublishing.com

Photos: Anne Bowers, Sheri Crispin, Nix Cuthill, Jean Dodds, Lynn Drumm, Mary Engstrom, Mike Fields, Karen Hotaling, Susan Merrick, Margie Rutbell, Al Sears, Faith Shariff, Julie Thompson, Nancy Topp, Dickie Walls, Trudy Weitkamp
Graphic Design: Lindsay Peternell

Library of Congress Cataloging-in-Publication Data

Dodds, W. Jean.
  The canine thyroid epidemic : answers you need for your dog / W. Jean Dodds, Diana Laverdure.
      p. cm.
  Includes bibliographical references and index.
  ISBN 978-1-61781-016-9
  1. Dogs--Diseases. 2. Thyroid gland--Diseases. 3. Thyroid gland. 4. Veterinary endocrinology. I. Laverdure, Diana, 1965- II. Title.
  SF992.E53.D63 2011
  636.7'089644--dc22
                            2010051308

ISBN: 978-1-61781-016-9

Printed in the U.S.A.

DEDICATION

To Issho—my inspiration to continue on the path of healing animals.

And to Shari—a sweet angel who shared our lives and home.

W. Jean Dodds, DVM

To Rodney—the only time words fail me is when I try to express the love, joy, and meaning that you have brought into my life. Namasté, my baby.

And to Chase—a shelter dog who never gave up hope. You are my hero and my inspiration. Thank you for rescuing me.

Diana R. Laverdure

Praise for *The Canine Thyroid Epidemic*

Jean Dodds has been my closest friend and mentor for over 17 years. Her enduring dedication to the health and welfare of dogs has been absolutely inspiring to all of us seeking viable health methods and longevity for our loving, furry companions. Jean has spent over 40 years researching, testing and lecturing about the impact the thyroid gland has on the health and longevity of dogs and other animals. There are few true revelations in veterinary medicine, and Jean's work is a major example. Her studies of thyroid dysfunction, behavioral problems, and autoimmune diseases has solved many undiagnosed canine problems, and has answered a lot of unanswered questions. As the founder of a large canine care group, I have seen the health of thousands dogs improve remarkably as a result of Jean's clinically tested discoveries. I've also seen seizures reduced or eliminated in dogs with canine epilepsy. Over the years five of my own dogs have benefited from Jean's experience. I don't know Diana, but she is clearly an amazing writer. She has combined academic credibility, case studies and Jean's voluminous research into a easy-to-read form that benefits veterinarians and dog guardians. This is a book that should find its way to the door of every veterinarian looking for answers to unanswered questions.
Joanne Carson, PhD, founder www.canine-epilepsy-guardian-angels.com

Dr. W. Jean Dodds has raised the awareness that canine hypothyroidism is not only about low thyroid hormone levels, but in fact, it's a continuum of disease that often begins with the immune destruction of the thyroid gland (autoimmune thyroiditis) and progresses over time to end-stage disease (hypothyroidism). And anywhere along the way clinical signs may appear; such as behavioral issues to classic signs such as lethargy and weight gain. In addition, Dr Dodds has made it clear to pet owners what signs to look for that may suggest thyroid dysfunction and what questions to ask their veterinarian about thyroid testing. Moreover, from her vast experience, she has outlined the many pitfalls that can lead to a wrong diagnosis such as assuming normal thyroid hormone levels rule out thyroid dysfunction. Not only is this book a great "eye opener" for pet lovers but also should serve as a reference for veterinarians whether they are in veterinary school or have many years experience in private or university practice.
Rhett Nichols, DVM, ACVIM (Internal Medicine), senior educator in veterinary endocrinology.

A must read book to all dog lovers!!!! Dr. Jean's knowledge is a breath of fresh air and a life saver for our beloved 4-legged "children."
Tamar Geller, renowned dog coach and best seller author of *The Loved Dog* and *30 Days To A Well-Mannered Dog.*

There's probably no one in the dog world who garners as much respect from all quarters as Dr. Jean Dodds. She is widely known for her uncompromising standards in research and her relentless devotion to the welfare of the canine species. She is truly a household name amongst dog owners and veterinarians alike.

Her latest work alarms and alerts us to an epidemic of thyroid disease of staggering proportions. It alarms us as we witness the early age at which the disorder now commonly appears, and alerts us to how commonly we aggravate the problem through breeding, vaccination and feeding practices.

Aggression, anxiety disorders, skin disease, seizures, cruciate ligament tears, food allergies, inflammatory bowel disease – the diversity of conditions that Dr. Dodds has linked to hypothyroidism is truly eye-popping. But take heart. The numerous cases studies showing their amenability to proper thyroid testing and hormone supplementation are a beacon of hope for veterinarians and owners that often feel defeated by these conditions.

This book may be historic within veterinary medicine. The large number of dog owners that read this book will be armed like never before with the ability to distinguish an enlightened professional opinion from one based on outdated dogma. The publication of this book may thus mark a watershed moment in veterinary history, where veterinarians en masse finally adopt the most current research on thyroid disease and vaccination practices, lest they otherwise fall short of the bar of professional competence this work is setting.

Steve Marsden, DVM, senior educator in complementary and alternative veterinary medicine, co-founder College of Integrative Veterinary Therapies, and Canadian Veterinary Medical Association, Small Animal Clinician of the Year, 2009.

The Canine Thyroid Epidemic is an amazing, life-saving gift to countless dogs and the people who love them. This expertly crafted guide provides the tools, advice and information needed to help dog parents navigate this complex, often misdiagnosed and misunderstood disease. From recognizing the signs to finding the right veterinarian to long-term management, I can't imagine a better resource. Thanks to Dr. Dodds and Ms. Laverdure for shedding light on this epidemic in terms we can all understand.

Melanie Monteiro, author *The Safe Dog Handbook.*

This is a terrific reference source for both the veterinary professional and the pet owner regarding thyroid disorders for our dogs. The book is organized with case studies and "take home points" at the end of each chapter for quick and easy future reference. It is so much more than just a reference book for thyroid disorders, it is a great reference book for pet owners for day to day care of dogs and cats. The authors discuss around the house toxins and other dangers to our pets including certain flea and tick preventatives.

The book is full of information regarding nutrition, diets and supplements to boost immune systems for our pets. It includes lists of food toxins to avoid and explains the importance of certain vitamins for our four legged friends.

Every pet owner should read the section on vaccinations and understand the risks of over-vaccination. The authors clearly explain how to avoid unnecessary vaccines with titer tests.
Ted W Eubank, Pinecrest Cavaliers, President of the Dallas Fort Worth Toy Dog Club and president of the Cavalier King Charles Spaniel Club of North Texas.

I really was thrilled to read this timely and important book! It was not only comprehensive, but easy to read and full of amazingly helpful information. It was lovely to have clear concise sections explaining thyroid function and simplifying testing and treatment parameters as they relate to different breeds of dogs. The charts and bullet point lists are very well designed to illuminate each point. This definitive book on canine thyroid issues is very professional, well-written and enlightening. A great way to learn vitally important information about this all-too-common condition in dogs today. Wonderful for veterinarians and owners!
Barbara Royal DVM, founder and owner of The Royal Treatment Veterinary Center and the go-to veterinarian for Oprah Winfrey.

TABLE OF CONTENTS

INTRODUCTION

Each year, countless dogs suffer needlessly—and many die—from an easily treatable condition known as canine thyroid disorder. Thyroid disease is sweeping through the canine community at such an alarming rate that it has reached epidemic proportions. Most dog guardians do not know how to spot the clinical symptoms of thyroid disease in their four-legged friends, and many veterinarians are unaware of how to properly test and diagnose their patients to determine if they suffer from a thyroid disorder. Unfortunately, this confusion on both the part of dog guardians and veterinary professionals sets up a "perfect storm" of misunderstanding, misdiagnosis, and mistreatment (or often complete lack of treatment) of canine thyroid disorder, and our dogs are the ones who suffer.

The goal of this book is ambitious: to unlock the mystery of thyroid disease in dogs so that our canine companions can live healthier, happier, and longer lives. Our audience is wide: dog enthusiasts; breeders; shelter operators; trainers; veterinarians; and everyone who loves and cares for dogs. We have laid out everything you need to better understand this confounding epidemic, and to take a proactive role in diagnosing and treating it in your own dog. Veterinary professionals will particularly benefit from Chapter 6 on testing, since the majority of veterinarians are still misinformed as to the necessary lab tests required and how to properly interpret them. Without this crucial piece of the puzzle, many veterinary professionals dismiss the clinical signs of thyroid disease, as these signs are often not supported by the inadequate testing that is currently the standard.

Chapter 1 delves right into the role of the thyroid and why it is essential to every aspect of health. It also presents a brief background of canine thyroid disease and why this misunderstood disorder has skyrocketed to epidemic proportions.

Chapter 2 is a must-read for anyone seeking to understand why thyroid disease develops in dogs and to understand its clinical signs. Much of the reason why thyroid disorder continues to confound dog caretakers and veterinarians alike is because its symptoms mimic a multitude of other diseases and conditions. This chapter will serve as a reference for anyone seeking a solid understanding of the symptoms presented by dogs suffering from canine thyroid disorder. It will empower laypeople with the knowledge to intelligently present the issue to their veterinarians, while professionals will find the quick-reference an invaluable tool during times when they are looking to reinforce their own instincts.

Chapter 3 is crucial to understanding how thyroid disorder affects the behavior of our canine companions. Millions of animals are euthanized each year due to "aberrant" behavior. This is sad when you consider that many of these animals are indeed suffering from an easily treatable medical condition. Dog enthusiasts of all types—and especially shelter managers and veterinarians—will benefit from understanding the connection between thyroid function and behavior, in all species. If even one dog's life is saved because of this chapter, we will feel as if we have done our jobs.

Chapter 4 builds upon the information provided about the physical and behavioral signs of thyroid disease to help you determine if your dog has a thyroid disorder. You will learn how to keep a detailed "canine health journal," which will help you to act as a more effective advocate for your dog when you take him to the vet.

Chapter 5 identifies risk factors that affect a dog's general well-being and tax his immune system, including environmental toxins, over-vaccination, prescription and non-prescription medications, chemical flea and tick preventives, and improper diet. Just as the toxins we introduce into our lives on a daily basis affect our general health and well-being, this is also true for our dogs. Reducing or eliminating these toxic influences is essential to creating companion animals with stronger immune systems that are better able to stave off canine thyroid disorder and other diseases.

Chapters 6, 7, and 8 cover what you need to know to actively participate in the care and management of your companion's thyroid disorder, from understanding which tests your dog should have, to properly administering your dog's medication, to tracking your dog's health over time. Veterinarians will learn that the "standard" laboratory tests they have been using for years to screen for thyroid disease are inadequate and often misleading, and that new testing and interpretive protocols must be followed if a consistently accurate diagnosis is to be achieved. Chapter 8 in particular discusses how to take control of your dog's health. You are his health care advocate, and he relies on you to act as his voice when it comes to interpreting and relaying any medical concerns to his veterinarian. Trusting your instincts and doing your own research are essential to ensuring your concerns are heard. Only when a true partnership exists between caretaker and veterinarian can our canine companions receive the high quality care they deserve.

Chapter 9 provides numerous case studies of dogs whose lives were turned around by the proper diagnosis and treatment of their thyroid disorder. Veterinarians resistant to diagnosing and treating canine thyroid disorder will hopefully gain insight and inspiration from these case studies—along with those included in each chapter—and understand that they have the ability to dramatically improve their patients' lives.

To make the book more user-friendly and educational, we have bolded the first use of key terms throughout the book and followed them immediately with definitions. Appendix A contains detailed information on related immune-mediated diseases, which every pet parent should be aware of in order to spot the signs in their own dog. We have also included a reference section detailing relevant research studies for veterinarians and others wishing to pursue the topic in greater detail.

There are eight pages of color photos between pages 88 and 89.

The more that dog lovers and veterinarians understand canine thyroid disorder, the better we can partner to diagnose and manage this confounding "epidemic." And when we do, the payoff will be spectacular. The quality of our dogs' lives will be greatly enhanced, their lifespan will be lengthened, innocent animals will cease from being euthanized due to misdiagnosed "aberrant" behavior, and our relationship with the dogs we love so much will be enriched.

We hope this book helps you understand the crucial role that the thyroid plays in your dog's health, and to identify potential problems that could be causing him to needlessly suffer. If, because of what you've learned between these pages, you can help your dog receive the proper medical care for his thyroid condition and enable him to live a healthy, happy, and long life, then we have done our job and we are very grateful.

CHAPTER 1

Canine Thyroid Disease:
A Misunderstood "Epidemic"

Casey, a three-and-a-half-year-old, intact male Golden Retriever, suddenly began showing signs of abnormal behavior. He became vocal, reactive to unknown dogs, easily excited, agitated, and restless. Over the period of a year, Casey became progressively more aggressive, going so far as to bite household members several times.

Casey's owners took him to the veterinarian, where blood tests confirmed that he suffered from **autoimmune thyroiditis,** an inherited autoimmune condition that progressively destroys the thyroid gland. The veterinarian placed him on **thyroxine** (also known as T4, the major hormone secreted by the thyroid gland) at a dose of 0.35 mg administered once daily.

Unfortunately, such a small dosage of thyroxine was inadequate for a dog of Casey's size. In fact, it would have been more appropriate for a dog of 20-25 pounds. In addition, the medication was being administered only once daily, when its **half-life** (the time it takes for the concentration of a drug to decrease by half in the blood), is 12-16 hours. This meant that, in addition to not receiving a high enough dosage of thyroxine, Casey was not benefiting from a 24-hour supply of the hormone circulating through his bloodstream.

When Casey showed no signs of improvement after two months on the therapy, his veterinarian decided to stop the thyroxine for two months and then retest him. During that time, Casey's aggressive behavior escalated. Upon retest a couple of months later, his blood work displayed the classical signs for **hypothyroidism** (low thyroid activity).

Fortunately for Casey, his veterinarian placed him back on the thyroxine—now at a correct dose and administered twice daily at 12-hour intervals. Casey showed almost immediate improvement, and after one year all of his blood thyroid hormone levels normalized. He was also neutered, so as not to pass along the inherited condition to any offspring. As long as he remains on the thyroxine therapy he will live a normal, healthy life, free from the negative effects of thyroid disease.

Casey was one of the lucky ones. All he needed was the proper thyroid replacement medication, given at the proper dosage, to normalize his aggressive behavior. But, had his veterinarian not run the appropriate tests and not determined a correct diagnosis and course of treatment, Casey might never have been diagnosed with thyroid disease. He might instead have seen a much grimmer fate, becoming one of the millions of dogs euthanized at shelters each year, many of whom have been relinquished due to "behavioral problems."

Casey is one of the huge numbers of dogs who, for a variety of reasons that we will discuss in this book, has fallen victim to the "epidemic" of canine thyroid disease. As we said, he is one of the lucky ones. Many others are not so fortunate. Their symptoms, which mirror so many other diseases and disorders, go overlooked or misdiagnosed. Their veterinarians still have not caught on to the proper testing protocols and perform inadequate blood screening. Or their blood work and their clinical signs contradict each other, confusing veterinarians and leading to erroneous conclusions.

In all of these instances, it is our beloved dogs who suffer.

From seizures and obesity to chronic infections, mood swings, and a wide range of other serious conditions, our dogs are being ravaged by a debilitating and confounding "epidemic." And, we humans have a lot to do with it. We are breeding them, feeding them, and rearing them toward a life of genetic weakness, ill health, and an inability to tolerate their toxic environments.

The question is, "Where do we go from here?" Are we going to perpetuate the misunderstandings and misconceptions of the past 30 years and allow "man's best friend" to continue to succumb to sickness? Or are we going to create a new awareness that will enable all of us—veterinary professionals and laypeople alike—to break the cycle of disease and give our dogs back the birthright of their health?

Dogs have been hanging out with humans and enriching our lives for more than 10 thousand years. This bond of caring and love has continued to blossom through the centuries, with our canine friends showering us with unconditional love, affection, and devotion. At the same time, they put their trust in us to do what is right for them. So now, as we strive for longer, healthier, and happier lives for ourselves, let's remember to include our canine friends in this quest.

This book will give you the knowledge, understanding, and tools you need to identify canine thyroid disease and proactively participate in your dog's diagnosis, treatment, and follow-up care. No longer will you feel helpless, knowing in your gut that something is wrong, but not knowing quite what it is. And no longer will your beloved canine have to endure needless suffering due to misunderstanding and misdiagnosis.

Let's start this journey toward our dogs' wellness by taking a closer look at the thyroid gland and its functions in the body.

What is the thyroid gland?

The thyroid gland is part of the **endocrine system,** the collection of glands that produces all of our body's hormones. Together, the endocrine glands control almost every cellular function. The glands that make up the endocrine system are:

- Pituitary (also called the major "master gland" because it controls several other glands)

- Hypothalamus

- Thyroid (a secondary master gland)

- Parathyroids

- Adrenals

- Pineal body

- Reproductive glands (ovaries and testes)

The **thyroid,** a secondary master gland to the pituitary gland, is located in the upper third of the neck. It is shaped roughly like a butterfly or a bow tie and is about the size of a lima bean. This, of course, varies slightly depending on the size of the dog (see Figure 1). The size of the thyroid gland increases during pregnancy.

Figure 1. The Thyroid Gland

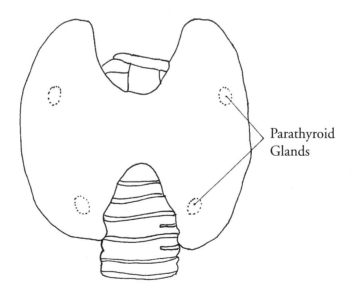

Parathyroid Glands

Production of thyroid hormones

A unique role of the thyroid gland is to take iodine supplied in food and use it to produce the hormones **T4** (thyroxine; tetraiodothyronine) and **T3** (triiodothyronine). Although 80-90% of the hormone produced in the thyroid gland is T4 and only 10-20% is T3, T3 is three-to-10 times more active than T4. Therefore, in order for the body's cells and tissues to benefit from thyroid hormone, T4 (which contains four iodine molecules) must be converted to T3 (which contains three iodine molecules) by losing an iodine molecule. This function is performed in the thyroid gland and other tissues by **de-iodinases** (enzymes that activate or deactivate thyroid hormone). About 80% of this conversion process occurs in the liver, with the remaining 20% taking place in the kidneys, spleen, muscles, skin, and central nervous system.

Since the liver plays a vital role in converting T4 hormone to T3, if either acute or chronic liver disease is present, the de-iodination process might be impaired and the T4 hormone that is present in the blood won't be effectively transmitted to the tissues as T3. This can result in people and animals who have what looks like normal blood thyroid levels still exhibiting clinical signs of hypothyroidism.

In addition, because thyroid hormone synthesis requires iodine, either a deficiency or an excess of iodine can profoundly affect thyroid function and promote autoimmune thyroiditis.

Functions of the thyroid gland

Both T4 and T3 hormones produced by the thyroid gland are used by the body to control **metabolism**, the speed at which the body transforms food into energy to perform its biochemical and enzymatic functions. They also act on and control the functions of virtually all of the body's cells, which include:

- Increasing **basal** (resting) metabolic rate

- Increasing the generation of body heat

- Increasing heart and respiratory (breathing) rate

- Controlling organ and tissue functions (protein, carbohydrate, and fat synthesis and enzyme, vitamin, and mineral production)

- Producing **calcitonin,** the hormone that plays a role in the regulation of calcium metabolism and blood calcium levels in the body

- Playing an important role in brain development

- Causing thickening of the uterine lining cells of females, in preparation for reproduction

The thyroid gland is an essential gland for life. If it is diseased, destroyed, or surgically removed, thyroxine hormone replacement therapy must be provided for the rest of the person's or animal's life in order for cellular activities to function properly.

The hypothalamic-pituitary-thyroid-axis

The hormone-producing actions of the thyroid gland are controlled by the pituitary gland and the hypothalamus, both of which are located in the head. Together, these glands make up what is referred to as the hypothalamic-pituitary-thyroid axis (see Figure 2).

Figure 2. The Hypothalamic-Pituitary-Thyroid Axis

Hypothalamus

CRH
Somatostatin
TRH

Pituitary

Anterior   Posterior

GH   ACTH

TSH

M-S
System   Adrenal   Vasopressin

Thyroid

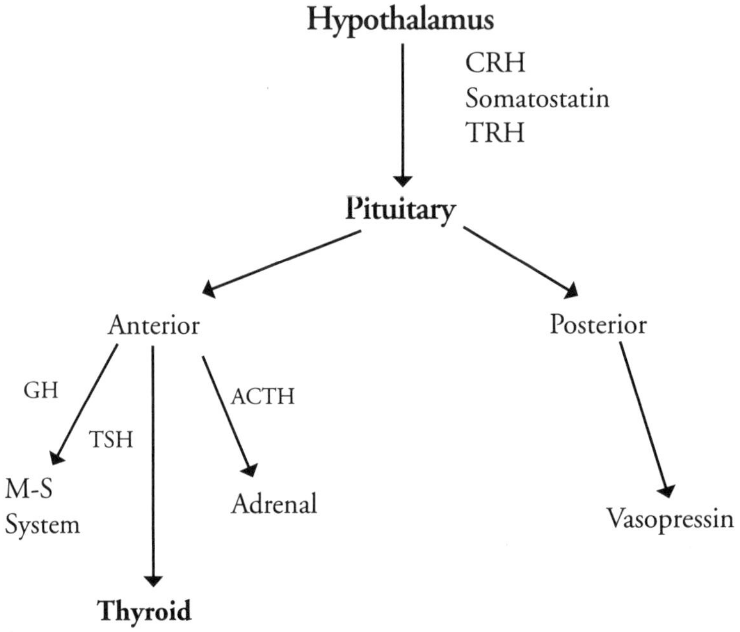

CRH = corticotrophin releasing hormone; Somatostatin = growth-hormone inhibiting hormone; TRH = thyrotropin releasing hormone; GH = growth hormone or somatotropin; TSH = thyroid stimulating hormone or thyrotropin; ACTH = adrenocorticotrophic hormone; M-S System = multiple sclerosis system; Vasopressin = antidiruetic hormone.

The pituitary gland produces and secretes **Thyroid Stimulating Hormone, or TSH,** also known as **thyrotropin.** The amount of thyrotropin released by the pituitary gland depends upon the amounts of **free T4** and **free T3** (the active forms of T4 and T3) circulating through the pituitary gland from the blood. The free T4 and free T3 signal the pituitary gland how much TSH to produce, thereby acting as a type of regulatory sensor of the body's needs for more thyroid hormone. When functioning properly, thyrotropin (TSH) secretion enables the thyroid to produce a steady level of T4 and T3 to circulate through the blood.

A major difference between humans and dogs is that while TSH controls about 95% of thyroid hormone regulation in humans, it controls only about 70% in dogs. The remainder of a dog's thyroid regulation is controlled by **growth hormone,** also known as somatotropin. Like TSH, growth hormone is also manufactured, stored, and secreted by the pituitary gland.

The hypothalamus produces and secretes **Thyrotropin Releasing Hormone (TRH),** the hormone that regulates the pituitary gland's production of TSH. In cold weather, for example, TRH is secreted at an increased rate. This in turn stimulates more TSH to be secreted by the pituitary gland, which increases thyroid hormone output to speed up metabolism and generate more body heat. When functioning properly, the hypothalamic-pituitary-thyroid axis is an elegant mechanism to control the body's metabolic activity. However, when that mechanism is not functioning optimally, it can result in a host of serious issues.

Body processes controlled by the hypothalamic-pituitary-thyroid axis include:

- Metabolism
- Cell growth
- Tissue function
- Enzyme production
- Organ function
- Brain development
- Mood regulation
- Growth and maturation
- Sexual processes
- Reproduction
- Cell oxygenation

What is canine thyroid disease?

Now that we've discussed what the thyroid gland does and its importance to the body's overall health, let's take a closer look at canine thyroid disease, what it is, and what causes it.

The first important thing to remember when talking about thyroid disease in dogs is that about 90% of the time it manifests as hypothyroidism. **Hypothyroidism** (underactive thyroid) occurs when the thyroid gland does not secrete enough T4 hormone. Symptoms of hypothyroidism also occur when the liver does not properly convert T4 into T3 which, as noted above, creates a hormone deficiency in the tissues. **Hyperthyroidism** (overactive thyroid) is rare in dogs, except in cases of thyrotoxicosis (overdosing on thyroid medication) or in the presence of thyroid cancer or cystic thyroid nodules.

As with Casey in our opening case study, up to 80% of canine hypothyroidism cases result from an inherited autoimmune condition known as **autoimmune (lymphocytic) thyroiditis,** which progressively destroys the thyroid gland. Autoimmune thyroiditis occurs when the body's **T-lymphocytes,** a type of white blood cell derived from the thymus gland which is responsible for fighting disease and infection, become programmed to destroy the thyroid gland. Since 1982, several studies (see References) have documented lymphocytic thyroiditis as the primary form of canine hypothyroid disease. The three breeds identified at that time to possess the highest incidences of thyroid autoantibodies (antibodies that mistakenly attack one's own tissues or organs) were the Great Dane, the Irish Setter, and the Old English Sheepdog—each of which is still listed today among the top 25 most affected breeds.

In addition to autoimmune thyroiditis, dogs are genetically predisposed to a number of **immune-mediated diseases** (also known as autoimmune diseases), diseases in which the body's own immune system attacks itself. This is also known as the "failure of self-tolerance." Other such diseases include:

- Rheumatoid arthritis
- Immune-mediated hemolytic anemia
- Immune-mediated thrombocytopenia
- Systemic lupus erythematosus
- Diabetes mellitus
- Addison's disease
- Pemphigus
- Immune complex glomerulonephritis
- Chronic active hepatitis
- Immune-mediated eye and central nervous system disorders
- Exocrine pancreatic insufficiency
- Myasthenia gravis

Canine autoimmune thyroid disease is very similar (and often identical), to Hashimoto's thyroiditis in humans, which has been shown to be associated with a certain group of genes known as the **MHC** (major histocompatibility complex) genes. A similar association with canine MHC genes in hypothyroid dogs has recently been reported in Doberman Pinschers, English Setters, and Rhodesian Ridgebacks. As of the date of this writing, research data have been collected from the DNA of another 10 dog breeds, and the analysis is nearing completion to identify the genetic markers associated with thyroiditis in these breeds (research of W. Jean Dodds in collaboration with Dr. Lorna Kennedy of the University of Manchester in the UK). The finding of at least one common genetic factor associated with thyroid disease in several canine breeds is very exciting, as it will hopefully clear the way to more accurately identify the cause of the disease and minimize passing it along to future generations.

Why is canine thyroid disease so misunderstood?

Even though hypothyroidism is the most frequently recognized canine endocrine disorder, it is still difficult to make a definitive diagnosis of the condition. Since the thyroid gland regulates metabolism of all of the body's cellular functions, reduced thyroid function can produce a wide range of clinical signs. Many of these signs mimic those of other disorders and illnesses, making recognition of a thyroid condition and proper interpretation of thyroid function tests confusing and problematic for veterinarians.

Misunderstanding of canine thyroid disease is compounded by the fact that formal study of it originated from what researchers already knew about the human disorder. Thyroid disease has been widely studied in people since the early 1900s. However, it wasn't until about 1980 that researchers began to question whether dogs could express similar thyroid dysfunction. During this time, they began to examine laboratory Beagles in an effort to better understand the canine thyroid gland. Not surprisingly, they recognized symptoms in dogs that mimicked the symptoms of human hypothyroid patients, including behavioral abnormalities, obesity, skin disorders, and intolerance to cold.

Much of this research with human thyroid patients has been beneficial to understanding canine hypothyroidism. We have learned through the study of mental and psychiatric disorders in people that thyroid hormones play an important role in brain development and function. These findings concerning the secretion, transport, and metabolism of thyroid hormones in the brain are also useful in helping us understand the thyroid/behavior connection in animals. However, in other instances, studying canine thyroid disease based on its human counterpart has proved misleading and confusing.

In order to confirm their clinical diagnosis of canine hypothyroidism, researchers studying the disease early on applied human testing protocols. They performed a **T4 blood** test (a blood test which measures the level of thyroxine in the blood in order to determine hyper- or hypothyroidism). However, for several reasons (see Chapter 6), T4 alone is an insufficient screening test for canine hypothyroidism and can provide misleading results. One such reason is that the half-life of both T4 and T3 in dogs is much faster than in people (every 12 to 16 hours in a dog versus every five-to-seven days in a person for T4, and every six-to-eight hours in a dog versus every 24 hours in a human for T3). This means that the level of active thyroid hormone circulating through a dog's blood remains at a constantly lower level than in a human's blood. Since the T4 test alone lacks the specificity and sensitivity to accurately detect canine thyroxine levels, it can lead to over-diagnosis of hypothyroidism.

In addition, although normal thyroid reference levels of healthy adult animals tend to be similar for most dog breeds, they do vary depending on age, breed, and even lifestyle. Puppies, for example, display higher basal thyroid levels than adults, because they are still growing and their bodies need extra hormones as they undergo the maturation process. The optimal thyroid levels for puppies are normally in the upper half of the adult reference ranges to 50% above the adult reference ranges. Conversely, the basal metabolism of geriatric animals is usually slowing, so optimal thyroid levels are likely to be closer to midrange or even slightly lower. Similarly, giant breed dogs naturally have lower basal thyroid levels, and Sighthounds as a group have the lowest levels of all the breed categories. We will discuss more on how to take these individual variations into account and the proper tests needed to check for canine hypothyroidism in Chapter 6.

For now, suffice it to say that by applying human testing standards and procedures to dogs, veterinary researchers have in effect been treating them as "furry little people." This has resulted in misinformation and inaccurate assumptions about canine hypothyroidism that still persist today, including that the T4 test alone is a reliable benchmark for accurate diagnosis. Unfortunately, it is our canine companions who suffer from misdiagnosis and non-diagnosis, which can, in the worst-case scenarios, prove deadly.

What are the signs of canine thyroid disease?

Normal thyroid function affects just about every aspect of a dog's health, including:

- Maintaining healthy skin and coat
- Maintaining proper body weight
- Promoting mental alertness and concentration
- Fighting infections
- Maintaining the body's temperature
- Controlling growth and maturation
- Facilitating normal reproduction

Since the thyroid gland regulates metabolism of all of the body's cellular activities, reduced thyroid function can produce a wide range of clinical signs, including:

Alterations in cellular metabolism
- Lethargy
- Weight gain
- Mental dullness
- Cold intolerance
- Exercise intolerance
- Mood swings
- Neurologic signs (polyneuropathy, stunted growth, seizures)
- Chronic infections
- Hyperexcitability

Neuromuscular problems

- Weakness
- Knuckling or dragging feet
- Stiffness
- Muscle wasting
- Laryngeal paralysis
- Megaesophagus
- Facial paralysis
- Head tilt
- "Tragic" expression
- Drooping eyelids
- Incontinence
- Ruptured cruciate ligament

Dermatologic diseases

- Dry, scaly skin and dandruff
- Chronic offensive skin odor
- Coarse, dull coat
- Bilaterally symmetrical hair loss
- "Rat tail"
- "Puppy coat"
- Seborrhea with greasy skin
- Seborrhea with dry skin
- Hyperpigmentation
- Pyoderma or skin infections myxedema

Reproductive disorders

- Infertility
- Prolonged interestrus interval
- Lack of libido
- Absence of heat cycles
- Testicular atrophy
- Silent heats
- Hypospermia

- Pseudopregnancy
- Aspermia
- Weak, dying, or stillborn pups

Cardiac abnormalities
- Slow heart rate (bradycardia)
- Cardiac arrhythmia
- Cardiomyopathy

Gastrointestinal disorders
- Constipation
- Diarrhea
- Vomiting

Hematologic (blood) disorders
- Bleeding
- Bone marrow failure
- Low red blood cells (anemia), white blood cells, platelets

Ocular (eye) diseases
- Corneal lipid deposits
- Corneal ulceration
- Uveitis
- Keratoconjunctivitis sicca or "dry eye"
- Infections of eyelid glands (Meibomian gland)
- Vogt-Koyanagi-Harada syndrome

Other associated disorders
- IgA deficiency
- Loss of smell (dysosmia)
- Loss of taste
- Glycosuria
- Other endocrinopathies, including chronic active hepatitis (adrenal, parathyroid, pancreatic)

The classical signs associated with hypothyroidism (significant weight gain, lethargy, cold intolerance, poor skin and hair coat) typically occur only after 70% or more of the thyroid tissue has been destroyed or damaged. Other changes, such as unexpected behaviors including lack of focus, aggression, passivity and phobias, subtle weight gain despite caloric restriction, and apparent food hypersensitivity or intolerance, can present themselves during the early phase of the disease.

To confuse the issue even further, dogs are contracting thyroid disease at a dramatically younger age. In the mid-1990s, the veterinary consensus was that if a dog was younger than five-to-seven years old, he was unlikely to suffer from hypothyroidism. Today, dogs ranging from as young as puberty (10, 12, or 14 months, depending on the breed) and up to two-and-a-half years old are regularly diagnosed with the disorder.

Why is canine thyroid disease an epidemic?

To answer that question, we must take a look at the breeding practices to which we humans have subjected our canine friends for more than a century. Since the 1800s, people have been continuously **inbreeding** (breeding close relatives such as brother/sister or parent/offspring) and **line-breeding** (breeding dogs that share a common distant, or not-so-distant, ancestor) in order to produce fixed physical, performance, or behavioral attributes.

The problem is that about 80% of canine hypothyroidism is the result of a genetically inherited autoimmune condition. This means that while we have been breeding our dogs to be docile companions or winning show dogs or superior athletes, we have in many instances also been breeding them toward a multitude of health maladies, including autoimmune thyroiditis.

Rather than making our pets suffer by passing along genetically inherited diseases through poor breeding practices, it is critical that we instead breed dogs with normal thyroid function. This holds true for performance and show dogs, as difficult as that might be for breeders to swallow. This makes it even more important to accurately diagnose canine hypothyroidism in its early stages, so that afflicted dogs can be removed from the breeding pool and neutered.

Further compounding the challenges to our dogs' immune systems is the constant barrage of chemical and environmental toxins to which they are exposed. We over-vaccinate them. We inundate them with chemical flea, tick, and heartworm preventives as well as non-steroidal, anti-inflammatory medications. We feed them nutrient-deficient diets. We expose them to chemical cleaning solutions, pesticides, and herbicides. Unfortunately, our desire to create the perfect breed "types" has resulted in dogs that are too genetically similar to fight off the stresses to their immune systems that are rampant in today's more toxic environment.

So, which breeds are at highest risk? Well, the clear "winner" is the English Setter, which has been highly inbred or line-bred. An astounding 43% of this lovable breed is afflicted with autoimmune thyroiditis.

While some breeds do have lower instances of canine thyroid disorder than others, there is no breed that has escaped this epidemic. Even mixed breeds are in jeopardy, since most are a combination of two or three inbred or line-bred breeds that are independently at risk.

Although the list of the top 25 breeds most affected with hypothyroidism is continually changing, it is generally composed of the following (listed alphabetically):

- Alaskan Klee Kai
- Beagle
- Borzoi
- Boxer
- Chesapeake Bay Retriever
- Cocker Spaniel
- Dalmatian
- Doberman Pinscher
- English Setter
- Eurasier
- German Wire-Haired Pointer
- Giant Schnauzer
- Golden Retriever
- Great Dane
- Havanese
- Irish Setter
- Kuvasz
- Labrador Retriever
- Leonberger
- Maltese
- Nova Scotia Duck Tolling Retriever
- Old English Sheepdog
- Rhodesian Ridgeback
- Shetland Sheepdog
- Staffordshire Terrier

Is hypothyroidism always a lifelong issue?

As with all diseases, there is variability involved with canine thyroid disorder. This book deals with general principles that apply to the vast majority of dogs. However, every animal is an individual, and there will be cases that fall outside of the mainstream.

In rare instances, both dogs and humans can develop what is known as "vanishing hypothyroidism," a form of thyroid disease that can spontaneously correct itself even without medical intervention. This syndrome is extremely rare and may be triggered in dogs by environmental contributing factors such as a rabies vaccines or iodine overdosing.

Since it is impossible to know which dog's hypothyroidism will spontaneously correct and which will not, the recommended step is to begin a course of thyroid replacement therapy and have the dog's hormone levels retested regularly. If your dog happens to have a rare case of vanishing hypothyroidism, you will soon figure this out via regular blood analyses. If his thyroid hormone levels return consistently high—even after you have reduced the dosage of thyroxine medication—you can gradually wean him off of the medication under the supervision of your veterinarian.

Physical issues causing hypothyroidism

Other physical issues that can cause the clinical signs of hypothyroidism include the following:

Selenium deficiency

Selenium is a mineral that plays an important role in the body's conversion of T4 into T3. Selenium deficiency in both humans and dogs will produce clinical signs of hypothyroidism, even though the patient's blood levels of thyroid hormones will appear perfectly normal. This makes it confusing to veterinarians who rely strictly on blood analysis to confirm canine thyroid disease, because they find themselves with a dog that appears outwardly hypothyroidic, but who tests normal.

Adrenal exhaustion syndrome

Adrenal exhaustion (also called **adrenal fatigue**) occurs when the **adrenal gland,** the gland which produces cortisol in response to stress, is over-stimulated and cannot function properly. Adrenal exhaustion is typically a transient condition and can result in impaired activity of the master glands such as the thyroid. Once the reason for the adrenal exhaustion is resolved, thyroid function should return to normal. In the meantime, nutritional supplements that offer thyroid support may be used and can prove beneficial.

Many human doctors, as well as veterinarians, resist prescribing thyroid treatment in cases of adrenal exhaustion, because they are not technically treating a thyroid disorder, they are treating a temporary adrenal malfunction syndrome. To that, we say if the patient shows marked improvement with thyroid hormone replacement and/or nutritional thyroid support, then why withhold appropriate and beneficial therapy? The fact remains that you are treating a thyroid-responsive disease—and the patient is getting better!

There are still some veterinary professionals and non-veterinary dog enthusiasts (such as breeders) who dismiss the concept of treating thyroid-responsive disorders with thyroid replacement therapy or thyroid support. These people insist that the results achieved with therapy in such instances are purely anecdotal. However, periodic monitoring of such cases shows that they are *not* anecdotal. Treating thyroid responsive disorders such as adrenal exhaustion, concurrent bone marrow failure or dysfunction, and aberrant behavior using thyroid replacement therapy has been *experientially* proven to work in repeated case studies (see References).

Congenital Hypothyroidism with Goiter (CHG)

The form of canine hypothyroidism discussed in this book should not be confused with Congenital Hypothyroidism with Goiter (CHG), a rare inherited endocrine disorder present in humans and dogs. CHG presents at or soon after birth, in contrast with the much more common adult onset form of hypothyroidism that we will address. In humans, untreated congenital hypothyroidism causes severe mental and physical retardation. However, early diagnosis and immediate treatment allows affected infants to lead normal lives. Every infant born in most countries is tested for this disorder as part of a publicly funded newborn screening program.

In dogs, CHG disease was originally described in the Giant Schnauzer breed in 1991, and more recently occurred in Toy Fox Terriers in New Zealand and North America. It is inherited as a simple autosomal recessive trait, which means that male and female pups can be affected, and both sexes can be asymptomatic carriers of the trait. Breeding two such carriers together will produce some affected (25% chance), some carriers like the parents (50% chance), and some genetically normal (25%) offspring. The affected puppies are homozygous (have two identical affected gene copies) for the defective CHG gene, asymptomatic carriers are heterozygous (one normal and one affected gene copy) for the CHG gene, and normal puppies are homozygous normal and have no copies of the CHG gene.

A similar acquired (non-heritable) clinical syndrome has been reported in a litter of Golden Retriever puppies born to a bitch that was supplemented inappropriately with kelp during late gestation and lactation. In this case, the CHG was caused by the high level of iodine in the kelp, which was toxic to the thyroid glands of the fetal and newborn pups.

This hereditary defect is fatal, and so is self-limiting, as affected puppies die shortly after birth or within the first three weeks of life. Affected puppies do not move around normally and may appear to have abnormally large heads. Even with special care, puppies survive to about three weeks of age, do not open their eyes, their ear canals remain very small, and the coat hair is abnormally bristly. A swelling soon appears on the underside of the neck and continues to enlarge. There is also delayed lengthening of bones in the legs, spine, and face which causes dwarfism. While most of these changes can be prevented or controlled by early diagnosis and daily oral thyroxine administration, the goiter continues to enlarge and eventually constricts the airway.

In the Toy Fox Terrier breed, the genetic defect causing CHG was found to be due to a mutation in the thyroid peroxidase gene. **Thyroid peroxidase** is an enzyme involved in the production of thyroid hormone and attaches iodine molecules to thyroglobulin protein. An accurate and reliable genetic DNA-based screening test has been developed for this defect in Toy Fox Terriers. Breeders can avoid producing more affected offspring if they only breed a dog that has produced the disease (i.e., an obligate carrier of CHG) to one that has tested to be free of the defective gene. Then, in the next generation, only clear testing offspring from this type of mating should be used for breeding.

Take home points

- Canine thyroid disorder is an "epidemic" affecting huge numbers of companion dogs each year.

- Undiagnosed or misdiagnosed canine thyroid disorder results in unnecessary illness and possible death.

- The thyroid gland is the second "master gland" to the pituitary gland. It is part of the body's endocrine system, the collection of glands that produces all of our body's hormones.

- The endocrine glands control almost every cellular function of our bodies.

- The thyroid gland uses iodine supplied in food to produce the hormones T4 (thyroxine; tetraiodothyronine) and T3 (triiodothyronine). These hormones control all of the body's metabolic functions.

- Although about 80-90% of the hormone produced by the thyroid gland is T4, it is T3 that is actively used by the cells and tissues to produce biochemical and enzymatic functions. T4 is converted into T3 by taking away an iodine molecule.

- Canine thyroid disease almost always manifests as hypothyroidism (low thyroid activity).

- About 80% of canine hypothyroidism is autoimmune thyroiditis (the result of a genetically inherited autoimmune disease).

- One or more common genetic factors are now being studied in dogs to determine at-risk breeds.

- Although there are a variety of similarities between canine thyroid disorder and human thyroid disease, there are also many differences that warrant separate study. Dogs are not "furry little humans."

- Many of the signs of canine thyroid disorder mimic other diseases and disorders, confusing veterinarians and making a definitive diagnosis difficult.

- The practice of inbreeding and line-breeding dogs to produce a fixed "type" has magnified the genetic nature of the disease.

- Although some breeds are more susceptible to canine thyroid disease than others, no breed is immune. Even mixed breeds are at risk.

- Although most of the time hypothyroidism in dogs is a lifelong issue, there are cases of "vanishing hypothyroidism," a form of thyroid disease that can spontaneously correct itself without medical intervention.

- Dogs are individuals. This book will help you to recognize the general principles of canine thyroid disorder so that you can help your dog—whether his condition "fits the mold" or not.

CHAPTER 2

Dogs in Decline:
Thyroid Disease and
Today's Canine Population

As we noted in Chapter 1, there is no dog breed—not even the lovable mixed breed—that is immune from the myriad of disorders related to canine thyroid syndrome. Genetics, breeding practices, and environmental stressors have all combined to tax the immune systems of our canine friends, leaving them susceptible to a disease that is the new "doggy epidemic." To top it off, the clinical signs of canine hypothyroidism can mimic such a wide variety of physical disorders and diseases that accurate diagnosis is confusing, even completely eluding veterinarians.

So, what's a pet parent to do? Fortunately, plenty! The first step in helping your hypothyroid dog is to be able to recognize the signs of canine hypothyroidism so that you can play a proactive role in his diagnosis. In this chapter, we will show you the "Top 10 Signs" of thyroid disorders in dogs and the common conditions related to canine hypothyroidism. We will also discuss the relationship between hypothyroidism and immune-mediated diseases so that you will be better prepared to discuss your dog's thyroid and its relationship to his overall health with your veterinarian.

Although many aspects of canine thyroid disorder differ from the human condition, it's interesting that both people and dogs share the same "Top 10" clinical signs of hypothyroidism—although not in the same order of prominence.

Top 10 signs of hypothyroidism in people and dogs

1. Weight change in the face of restricted caloric intake
Has your canine companion been packing on the pounds, even though you've been cutting back on his doggy treats? His weight gain could be due to hypothyroidism. Many dog parents become frustrated when they restrict their pet's caloric intake by placing him on a low fat, senior, or other calorie-restricted diet, yet he continues to gain weight (or does not lose weight). Weight gain is the number two sign of

hypothyroidism in humans, but it takes top spot for dogs. So, if you are counting your canine's calories (which is different than restricting the *volume* of his food) and he is still too pleasingly plump, this could signal hypothyroidism. (See Photos 1 and 2 in the insert.)

2. Hair and skin changes

Just one look at an unusual clump of hair clogging the shower drain would raise concerns for a person, and understandably so. Our hair and skin are perhaps the most visible signs of our health. The same holds true for our dogs. Whereas a soft, shiny coat radiates good health, hair and skin abnormalities often signal a deeper problem lurking within the body. This is certainly the case with thyroid disease. Common skin and coat issues in hypothyroid dogs include excessive shedding, dry, dull, brittle coat, and **hyperpigmentation** (darkening) of the skin. You might also find it easy to pull out your dog's hair, or he might develop what is known as a "puppy coat," which occurs when the outer hairs fall out, leaving just the soft undercoat. Hair loss around the trunk, thighs, and tail are also common. In cases of bacterial infections, such as staphylococcal "staph" pyoderma (see below), the skin can also become inflamed, itchy, and foul smelling. (See Photos 3 through 9 in the insert.)

3. Fatigue

If you're thinking of renaming your canine friend "Spud" because all he wants to do is hang out like a couch potato, there could be more to his low energy level than mere laziness. Nobody knows your dog better than you do, so if he seems to have lost the spring in his step or becomes uncharacteristically exhausted after a light game of fetch, please take note. Fatigue is a very common early warning sign of hypothyroidism in dogs and warrants investigating. When thyroid activity decreases, so does the body's metabolism. As metabolism slows, the body becomes fatigued. Fortunately, with the proper hormone replacement therapy, you will have your furry playmate back in no time.

4. Depression and anxiety

It's not so easy to tell when an animal is depressed, but you know your dog's behavior better than anyone and should trust your instincts. If your normally calm and easygoing pet suddenly displays bursts of panic, phobias, or anxiety, you should take that as a warning sign. The same holds true for a happy, active dog who seems to have lost his *joie de vivre* (joy of life) and no longer shows interest in doing the things he used to enjoy. The key is to watch for changes in your dog's usual behavior patterns. Even though he can't tell you if he is depressed or anxious, you will likely notice the signs almost immediately.

5. Family history

Family history is an important factor for both humans and animals in any genetically inherited disease, and this is certainly true with autoimmune thyroiditis, the inherited form of hypothyroidism. In the case of dogs, "family" could refer to whether or not the animal belongs to a high-risk breed. It could also, as with inbreeding and/or line-breeding, refer to the health history of the dog's closest relatives, such as parents, sisters, brothers, or cousins. It's important to understand that while some animals are at higher risk, no dog breed—not even crossbred or feral animals—is immune.

Feral animals that have been rescued and adopted from animal shelters could come from an inbred situation where one male dog controls all of the females in a particular geographic area. If this male is afflicted with hypothyroidism, some of his offspring are also at genetic risk. We can't know for certain if this is the case, but the important thing is not to assume that only purebred dogs are at risk and dismiss the possible signs of thyroid disease because your dog is a crossbreed. Crossbreeds originate from their breed ancestors, and they come to the table—for better or worse—with those same genes.

6. Gastrointestinal (bowel) problems

Both humans and dogs experience thyroid function-related gastrointestinal (GI) issues, but the symptoms differ greatly between our canine friends and us. Whereas hypothyroid people most commonly suffer from extreme constipation, dogs exhibit more uneven gastrointestinal signs that commonly include a combination of diarrhea, vomiting, and possible constipation. Eliminating aggravating dietary factors such as wheat, corn, and soy may help to control your dog's inflammatory bowel syndrome (IBS), which is also known as inflammatory bowel disease (IBD). We will discuss nutritional effects on our dogs' health and the relationship to thyroid disorders in Chapter 5.

7. Menstrual irregularities and fertility problems

Hypothyroid dogs do not suffer from the menstrual irregularities that are common in people. This is because intact female dogs experience heat (estrus) cycles typically every five-to-seven months, and they do not shed their uterine lining as women do at the completion of a monthly cycle. However, both canine sexes do exhibit thyroid function-related fertility and other reproductive problems.

Hypothyroidism in female dogs has been reported to cause a variety of reproductive issues, including erratically spaced heats, infertility, abortion, and stillbirth. **Pseudopregnancy** (false pregnancy)—which includes milk flow from the mammary glands and abdominal swelling—is also common. Hypothyroidism also affects male fertility, resulting in possible low sperm levels and decreased libido.

In research studies of healthy bitches that had previously delivered full-term litters, hypothyroidism was intentionally induced by radioactive iodine administration. An equal number of healthy control bitches was studied. After breeding, both groups were evaluated for the following: pregnancy, fetal re-absorption, **gestation** (pregnancy) length, litter size, duration and strength of uterine contractions at delivery, interval between delivery of pups, **viability** (vigor) of pups at birth, neo-natal survival, and weight of pups at birth through four weeks of age. All of the females in both groups delivered full-term litters.

Somewhat surprisingly, significant differences between the groups were only noted in three areas: the duration of uterine contractions (which were longer and weaker in the hypothyroid group); viability scores and birth weight (which were lower in pups from hypothyroid mothers); and the number of neo-natal deaths (which were higher in litters from hypothyroid bitches). So, although hypothyroidism of relatively short duration did not affect fertility in this experimental study, it did prolong the birth process and reduce post-birth puppy survival.

8. Neck discomfort or enlargement

This common sign of thyroid disease in humans is not seen very often in dogs, since it is usually associated with *hyper*thyroidism. As we discussed in Chapter 1, hyper-thyroidism is rare in dogs. However, in the very early inflammatory phase of autoim-mune thyroiditis, it is possible for a dog's thyroid gland to swell. During this period, which typically lasts two-to-four months, an overactivity of the thyroid gland occurs, creating a brief inflammatory "thyroid storm." This overactivity causes the thyroid to temporarily enlarge before it begins to shrink (once the gland starts becoming progres-sively destroyed). This condition is *not* the same as "thyroid storms" in people, which refers to a life-threatening form of *hyper*thyroidism.

9. Muscle and joint pain

In humans, aches and pains in the muscles and joints, tendonitis, carpal tunnel syn-drome in the arms/hands, and tarsal tunnel in the legs can all point to an undiagnosed thyroid problem. Our dogs, too, can suffer from muscle and joint pains, and weak-ness. Hypothyroid animals can also experience loose joints, which lead to **patellar sub-luxation** (partial dislocation of the kneecaps) from weakened or torn **cruciate** (cross-shaped) ligaments. Hip joint **laxity** (looseness) can also be seen in hypothy-roidism, especially in females that are X-rayed during a heat cycle (because increased estrogen levels also promote hip joint laxity).

10. Cholesterol issues

In people, high cholesterol that does not respond to lifestyle changes or medication can signal undiagnosed hypothyroidism. However, high cholesterol is not generally a classical sign of canine hypothyroidism. Although it is possible for dogs to exhibit high cholesterol at the end stages of this disease, when the thyroid is mostly destroyed, it is not an accurate indicator of hypothyroidism in its earlier phases. So, a finding of normal cholesterol levels via laboratory testing should never be used as a determinant to rule out canine hypothyroidism.

If you suspect hypothyroidism

It would certainly be convenient if our dogs could say, "Hey, I think my recent gas-trointestinal issues, combined with my sudden lack of desire to play fetch, might be indicative of hypothyroidism. Plus, I've been feeling a little depressed lately!" Of course, since they *can't* tell us how they're feeling, it's our job to get to know their nor-mal physical and behavioral signs and recognize when things look "not quite right."

If you suspect your dog is suffering from hypothyroidism, it's best to follow your instincts and schedule a complete physical examination—including a comprehensive blood workup—with your veterinarian. If your veterinarian is reluctant to make a diagnosis of thyroid disorder, in spite of the clinical signs, ask if she would be willing to work with you to prescribe hormone replacement on a trial basis of, say, six weeks, to see if your dog responds. If your veterinarian sees that your dog's symptoms disappear or improve from the trial therapy, she will hopefully be motivated to continue the treatment and to help many other dogs in a similar situation.

However, if you try reasoning with your veterinarian and she still refuses to try the hormone replacement on a trial basis, you might politely explain that you understand, and that you intend to take your dog for a second opinion. We will discuss more on how to talk to your veterinarian and how to proactively care for your dog throughout the remainder of the book. For now, suffice it to say that your dog is depending on you to look out for him and to do what's best. That might mean following your instincts right out of your current vet's office and into the office of one who is willing to listen to your concerns and evaluate your pet from a **holistic** point of view, an approach to wellness that looks at all aspects of your dog's well-being, including physical, emotional, social, and environmental.

Other conditions associated with hypothyroidism

Since the thyroid affects the functioning of just about every aspect of the body at a cellular level, there are a number of related conditions that manifest in both people and animals with thyroid disorder. The following are common conditions associated with hypothyroidism:

Adrenal exhaustion

As we discussed in Chapter 1, adrenal exhaustion, or fatigue, occurs when the adrenal gland becomes over-stimulated and cannot properly produce hormones, most notably cortisol. Adrenal exhaustion can negatively impact the activity of the master glands such as the thyroid.

Osteoporosis

As we age, we all worry about **osteoporosis,** a loss of bone density, and the resulting symptoms, such as bone pain and **fractures** (broken bones). Our dogs are also susceptible to osteoporosis as a result of thyroid dysfunction. Since thyroid hormones are involved in maintaining bone density, hypothyroidism can progressively lead to the resorption of calcium from bones and replacement of the tissue support framework within bone with fibrous connective tissue.

Staphylococcal pyoderma

Staphylococcal pyoderma (pyoderma means "pus on the skin") is a bacterial skin infection of dogs caused by the Staphylococcus intermedius (recently renamed as Staphylococcus pseudointermedius) bacteria. Dogs with thyroid disorder can suffer from pyoderma and other skin infections, such as chronic **folliculitis** (an infection of one or more hair follicles), and even several types of mange and fungal infections, because hypothyroidism lowers the ability of the body's immune system to defend against such secondary infections.

Note: This is a different subtype of Staphylococcus than that affecting people (Staphylococcus aureus). The methicillin resistant Staphylococcus aureus (MRSA) strains of this bacterium that some people carry do not typically affect dogs nor are they usually carried by dogs.

Heart disease

Since thyroid hormone regulates heartbeat, decreased thyroid activity can result in **bradycardia** (slow heart rate). The heart rate of a dog with bradycardia related to hypothyroidism is typically below 65 beats per minute (bpm), whereas a normal dog's heart rate is between 70 and 140 beats per minute. If left untreated, hypothyroidism can also lead to **dilated cardiomyopathy,** an enlargement of the heart's left, right, or both ventricles. Dilated cardiomyopathy decreases the amount of blood pumped out with each beat and is a leading cause of congestive heart failure, which can be fatal. It is more commonly seen in certain larger dog breeds, especially in males. Predisposed breeds include:

- Afghan Hound
- American Cocker Spaniel
- Boxer
- Dalmatian
- Doberman Pinscher
- English Springer Spaniel
- Great Dane
- Irish Wolfhound
- Newfoundland
- Old English Sheepdog
- Portuguese Water Dog
- Saint Bernard
- Saluki
- Scottish Deerhound

Case study

Ben, a four-year-old, black-and-tan American Cocker Spaniel show and obedience champion, was presented to one of the authors (WJD) for sudden aggression towards a local veterinarian who was opening Ben's mouth to examine his tonsils. Ben had been very healthy until he appeared to have a brief seizure, which prompted the visit to his regular veterinarian. Upon observing him, the veterinarian's first impression was that Ben was in outstanding condition, including having a lustrous, long, flowing coat. However, Ben appeared "dopey" and even fell asleep in the examination room. Ben's physical examination was unremarkable, except for a very slow heartbeat of 55 bpm. The veterinarian drew blood for a complete health checkup, including thyroid antibody profiling. Lo-and-behold, Ben was found to have heritable autoimmune thyroiditis, which had progressed to hypothyroidism.

Ben's bradycardia, in addition to his seizure-like episode and his biting of the local veterinarian (see Chapter 3 for more on thyroid disorder and aberrant behavior) were early signs of the disorder. His clinical and behavioral issues resolved rapidly after he began thyroid replacement therapy.

Cold intolerance

Does your dog like to lounge by the fireplace in the winter? He may just enjoy the warm glow, or he might be telling you that his thyroid is not functioning properly. Since one of the thyroid gland's many jobs is to regulate body temperature, when this metabolic process is impaired due to hypothyroidism, dogs (as well as people) will experience unusual sensations of cold in their extremities (in a dog's case, his paws), as well as a general intolerance to the cold.

Anemia

Anemia results from low red blood cells or low **hemoglobin** (a protein in red blood cells that carries oxygen), or both. Anemia is one of the most common related conditions seen in dogs with hypothyroidism. Canine thyroid disorder can lead to related anemia because it impairs the production of new red blood cells. Autoimmune diseases such as autoimmune hemolytic anemia can be primary, or secondary, to hypothyroidism, and lead to related anemia because it causes **hemolysis** (a breakdown of red blood cells). Anemic dogs may appear weak or listless, with pale gums that have lost their normal pink color.

Iodine levels

As we discussed in Chapter 1, iodine is essential to the production of thyroid hormones T4 and T3, so it's easy to understand how either too much or too little iodine could disrupt normal thyroid function. Remember that T4 contains four iodine molecules and T3 (the form most utilized by the cells and tissues) has three iodine molecules. When either people or animals don't get enough iodine in their diets, the thyroid can't produce enough hormones. This disrupts the body's normal metabolic processes, resulting in hypothyroidism. It's important to point out, however, that autoimmune thyroiditis, the inherited (and most common) form of canine hypothyroidism, is *not* related to iodine deficiency. So, it's risky to automatically supplement a hypothyroid dog's diet with iodine, as many people do (such as in the form of kelp). Supplementation can result in excessive iodine intake, which can in turn cause the thyroid gland to overproduce T4 and T3. This can provoke an immune-mediated response in the body, where the immune system actually attacks the thyroid gland and inhibits hormone output. Such a response can suppress thyroid levels by up to 25%, causing hypothyroidism as well as autoimmune thyroiditis.

Candida (yeast)

Candida *albicans* is a type of yeast microorganism. Yeast is normally present in the digestive tracts of healthy humans and animals, where it lives alongside the **friendly flora** (beneficial bacteria), which protect the lining of the intestines. If a dog's digestive tract is healthy, these potentially harmful yeast organisms are kept in check by the friendly bacteria in his gut. When the friendly bacteria are somehow damaged or destroyed, the natural "ecosphere" of the dog's intestinal tract is disrupted. This can occur due to a variety of reasons, including antibiotics, vaccines, food intolerance, and hypersensitivity. This can result in a yeast infection that can spread to other parts of his body, causing a variety of symptoms such as vaginal, ear, and foot yeast infections, and fungal skin infections.

Head tilt

Head tilt results from a disease of the **vestibular system** (the parts of the inner ear which help the body to maintain balance and contribute to its sense of spacial awareness). When the vestibular system is not working properly, both people and animals experience vertigo and feel imbalanced or dizzy. Geriatric and middle-aged dogs are most susceptible to a disorder known as Peripheral Vestibular Syndrome, which is sometimes linked to hypothyroidism. With Peripheral Vestibular Syndrome, pressure on the peripheral nerves can lead to paralysis of the facial muscles and/or head tilt, as well as bizarre eye motions and **vestibular disease** (balance disruption).

Thyroiditis and immune-mediated diseases

A healthy immune system is designed to protect animals and humans from harmful foreign invaders, such as those that cause disease and infection. An immune-mediated disease occurs when the immune system becomes unable to distinguish between a foreign invader and a natural part of itself, such as an organ, tissue, or other substance normally present in the body. The body becomes, in effect, "intolerant" of itself. This intolerance results in an autoimmune reaction in which the immune system malfunctions and begins to attack a part of itself that it perceives as threatening the health of the body.

Susceptibility to autoimmune diseases has a strong genetic basis in both people and animals, although numerous viruses, bacteria, chemicals, toxins, and drugs can also trigger an autoimmune reaction. This principle is illustrated by the "threshold model" for inducing autoimmune disease in Figure 3. We will discuss more about the effects of environmental toxins on the body's immune system in Chapter 5.

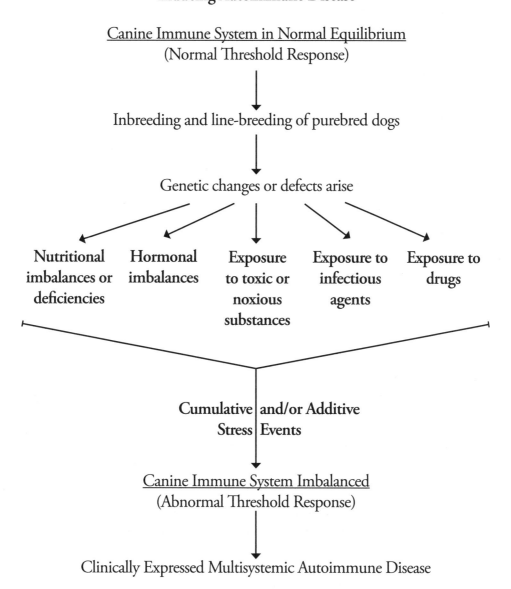

Figure 3. The Threshold Model for Inducing Autoimmune Disease

Canine Immune System in Normal Equilibrium
(Normal Threshold Response)

Inbreeding and line-breeding of purebred dogs

Genetic changes or defects arise

Nutritional imbalances or deficiencies · Hormonal imbalances · Exposure to toxic or noxious substances · Exposure to infectious agents · Exposure to drugs

Cumulative and/or Additive Stress Events

Canine Immune System Imbalanced
(Abnormal Threshold Response)

Clinically Expressed Multisystemic Autoimmune Disease

The four main factors that cause autoimmune disease in humans and animals are:

- Genetic predisposition
- Hormonal influences, especially of the sex hormones
- Infections, especially of viruses
- Stress

The most commonly recognized autoimmune disorders in dogs involve the following bodily systems listed below: (Note: Therapy is not discussed here, as your veterinarian will be the person to initiate therapy.)

- **Endocrine.** Thyroid glands/autoimmune thyroiditis, adrenal glands/Addison's disease, pancreas/juvenile diabetes mellitus

- **Hematologic.** Erythrocytes/immune-mediated or autoimmune hemolytic anemia, platelets/immune-mediated thrombocytopenia

- **Muscles.** Myasthenia gravis, dermatomyositis, masticatory muscle myositis (MMM), polymyositis

- **Joints.** Rheumatoid arthritis

- **Eyes.** Keratoconjunctivitis sicca, "dry eye" or KCS

- **Skin.** Pemphigus disorders, systemic lupus erythematosus, vitiligo

- **Kidneys.** Immune-complex glomerulonephritis, systemic lupus erythematosus

- **Bowels.** Inflammatory bowel disease

- **Central Nervous System.** Immune-complex meningoencephalitis

It's important to be aware of these autoimmune disorders so that you can monitor your own dog for signs. For a detailed description of each disorder, including the breeds most affected, see Appendix A.

Stress and hypothyroidism

When your dog senses stress, his adrenal glands release the hormone cortisol into the bloodstream (just as it does with humans). Although cortisol performs many important functions in the body, such as helping to regulate blood pressure and managing the release of insulin to maintain proper blood sugar levels, it is often referred to as the "stress hormone" because it is secreted in higher levels during the body's "fight or flight" reaction.

Increases of cortisol during stress are beneficial, as it gives the body that "burst of energy" needed to avoid potentially life-threatening situations. However, a constant increase in levels of cortisol in the bloodstream due to a chronic state of stress may suppress the pituitary gland's output of TSH. As we discussed in Chapter 1, TSH acts as a sensor to regulate the body's requirement for more thyroid hormone.

If you feel your dog might be suffering from canine thyroid disorder, take a look at the stressors in his life and see what you can do to manage or eliminate them. Common contributing factors to canine stress are:

Age

Every stage of a dog's life brings with it a different set of stresses. During early puppy-hood, weaning and separation from their mothers and littermates are stressful events, as is relocation to a new home. Next come the stresses of puberty, then adulthood and reproduction for those dogs who are not neutered or spayed. Finally, as an animal approaches and enters old age, there is another set of stressors that takes over.

Personal history

Is your pet a rescue or shelter dog? Did he join your family as a puppy or has he had to deal with the upheaval of "starting from scratch" in a new home later in life? Could he have even endured an abusive situation? Just as with people, our pets' personal histories affect their current stress levels. A dog that was once abandoned, for instance, might continue to suffer from separation anxiety every time he is left alone in the house.

Your family situation

Our canine companions are like emotional sponges, absorbing the atmosphere around them. You might have to ask yourself some tough questions here, such as whether your household environment generates a lot of stress. If so, you can bet that your dog is picking up on that negative vibe and that it's affecting his emotional well-being, too.

Your dog's family history

Just as people have family backgrounds, so do dogs. And, also like people, some are dealt a better hand in the family tree department than others. Some dogs have sketchy histories, others have no known family background (strays or rescues), and still others have amassed a proud family heritage and health history. It's curious, though, that many of the most influential show or performance dogs who are claimed to have had no history of abnormal disease or behavior in their family background then produce offspring with such disorders! This is akin to breeders stating that they must breed a dog with some documented fault because "it's the last of this prominent line of dogs around," when several others have made the same claim about this same blood line. Justification for breeding such dogs relies on the conscience and integrity of the breeder.

Pregnancy/postpartum

Physiological and even psychological stresses occur in both sexes when females go through heat cycles, especially with intact male dogs present. Additional stresses occur during and after pregnancy and lactation, with difficult pregnancy and **dystocia** (labor), poor milk production, and mastitis. The presence of neonatal or **perinatal** (around the time of birth) stillborns and weak, dying pups is stressful to the dam. Pseudopregnancy is also stressful to the body.

Foods that inhibit thyroid hormone production

Certain foods contain naturally occurring substances that can interfere with the thyroid gland's production of hormone. These substances are called **goitrogens,** which comes from the term **goiter,** an enlargement of the thyroid gland. The two main groups of goitrogen-containing foods are cruciferous vegetables and soy products. The grain millet is also mildly goitrogenic. Limit feeding of these foods if your dog displays signs of thyroid imbalance.

Research shows that the thyroid-disrupting substance in soy is the isoflavones. Soy isoflavones can block the activity of **thyroid peroxidase (TPO),** the enzyme found in the thyroid follicle cells where it helps convert the thyroid hormone T4 to T3. In human autoimmune thyroid disease, significant amounts of antibodies are produced against TPO as well as to thyroglobulin. By contrast, antibodies to TPO play a minimal role in the disorder for animals with thyroiditis.

In fact, research conducted on infants who were fed soy formulas found that these children were nearly three times more likely to develop autoimmune thyroid disease as adults due to their exposure to soy isoflavones.

As soybeans have become more commonly used as a source of high-quality vegetable protein in commercial pet foods, the question arises whether this potential source of dietary goitrogen could offer an explanation for the ever increasing incidence of feline hyperthyroidism throughout the world. The mechanism whereby soy affects thyroid metabolism is poorly understood, although many theories have been elucidated during the past 70 years. Soy isoflavones have weak estrogenic properties as well as effects on thyroid metabolism. The effects of soy on the thyroid gland are modified by dietary iodine. Therefore, iodine deficiency enhances the goitrogenic effects of soy, whereas iodine supplementation (e.g., kelp in modest amounts) is protective. However, the iodine concentration in commercial pet foods today is about three times the stated minimum requirement, which is a problem because excess iodine also inhibits thyroid function and promotes thyroiditis.

Another interesting relevant study of commercial dog foods determined the type and concentration of soy phytoestrogens. The conclusion of the study was that soybean fractions are commonly used ingredients in commercial dog foods, and the phytoestrogen content of these foods is high enough to have biological effects when eaten long-term. These effects can be both beneficial and deleterious. But, further investigations are needed to look at the effects of phytoestrogens on the immune response of puppies and adult dogs (e.g., thymic and immune abnormalities), effects on sex hormones (e.g., delayed puberty and infertility), and possible undesirable effects on skin and coat length and quality.

Most of us don't eat enough veggies. Heck, we've been told that since we were children, hiding our green beans under our mashed potatoes or sneaking our Brussels

2 — DOGS IN DECLINE

sprouts to our dog (which might not have been such a good idea if they had a thyroid condition!).

Cruciferous vegetables in particular are very healthy, thanks to naturally occurring compounds called isothiocyanates. Different cruciferous vegetables are rich in different isothiocyanates, which scientists believe are important in the prevention of cancer. However, these isothiocyanates, like the isoflavones in soy, reduce thyroid function by blocking the activity of thyroid peroxidase. So, if you think that your dog might be suffering from a thyroid problem, don't pile on the cabbage or cauliflower or any of the other veggies listed below:

- Broccoli
- Brussels sprouts
- Cabbage
- Casaba
- Cauliflower
- Kale
- Kohlrabi
- Mustard
- Rutabagas
- Radishes
- Turnips

Millet is an ancient grain that has been cultivated for thousands of years. It is a good source of key nutrients such as manganese, phosphorous, tryptophan, and magnesium. It is rich in insoluble fiber. In dog food, millet is often included in foods traditionally touted as "grain-free," since it is considered a healthier alternative to wheat. However, hypothyroid dogs should indulge sparingly in millet, since the hulls and seeds contain small amounts of goitrogens.

We will talk more about nutrition's effect on canine thyroid disease in Chapter 5 and also discuss the spectrum of food options best suited for hypothyroid dogs.

Thyroid and mental health

Behavioral and psychological changes have been associated with thyroid dysfunction in humans for several hundred years, but hypothyroidism also plays a key role in the mental health of our canine friends. Hypothyroid dogs—especially younger dogs with autoimmune thyroiditis—can display a wide variety of abnormal behaviors. Today, in spite of how animals have been bred and selected for their behaviors over several thousand years, millions of them are being destroyed annually due to behavioral problems.

With thyroid-related behavior issues, a quiet, well-mannered, and sweet-natured dog may suddenly show signs of moodiness, erratic temperament, lack of concentration, depression, mental dullness, anxiety, fearfulness, and other uncharacteristic behaviors. These changes can progress to sudden unprovoked aggressiveness in unfamiliar situations with other animals, people, and especially with children.

In the next chapter, we will discuss how diminished thyroid function affects behavior in dogs, how you can recognize thyroid-related behavioral changes, and what you can do to help your canine buddy return to his happy, healthy, sweet-natured self.

Take home points

- Knowing the "Top 10 Signs" of canine hypothyroidism is essential in helping you play a proactive role in your dog's diagnosis.

- You know your dog best. If you think something is wrong, follow your instincts and get it checked out.

- Because the thyroid affects the functioning of just about every aspect of the body at a cellular level, there are a number of related conditions that manifest in people and animals with thyroid disorder. Becoming familiar with these related conditions will help enable you to draw a possible connection to your dog's thyroid.

- The four main factors that cause autoimmune disease are genetic predisposition, hormonal influences (especially of the sex hormones), infections (especially of viruses), and stress.

- Dogs are susceptible to a wide variety of autoimmune disorders involving just about every bodily system.

- Stress contributes to immune-mediated diseases including autoimmune thyroiditis. Try to identify the stressors in your dog's life and manage or eliminate them.

- Goitrogenic foods are foods that contain naturally occurring substances that can interfere with the thyroid gland's production of hormone. Cruciferous vegetables and soy products are the most goitrogen-containing foods. Millet is also mildly goitrogenic. It is advised to limit the feeding of goitrogenic foods in dogs who shows signs of thyroid imbalance.

- Hypothyroidism plays a key role in the mental health of our canine friends and can contribute to a host of uncharacteristic and undesirable behaviors.

CHAPTER 3

Thyroid Disorder and Aberrant Behavior

It's sad that millions of dogs each year are abandoned at shelters or euthanized due to behavioral issues—especially when a significant number may be attributed to an easily treatable thyroid disease or dysfunction. Our canine friends give us their unconditional love every day, yet we are all too often ready to dismiss their undesirable behavior as some sort of emotional "defect" on their part, rather than a physical condition over which they have little or no control. The goal of this chapter is lofty: to spare as many innocent dogs as possible from the harsh fate of abandonment—or even the death sentence of euthanasia—by educating those who love them on how to spot thyroid-related behavioral issues, and manage or reverse them with the proper treatment.

Take Tater, a three-year-old, neutered male Bull Terrier. Tater was originally diagnosed with Rage Syndrome and had been in several homes after developing behavioral issues. Tater's problems were compounded by the fact that he is deaf. His current home is with an animal health technician, where everything was fine for a few months. Then, suddenly, Tater began to jump up without warning during sleep and roar like a lion. He attacked any person, animal, or thing nearby, and then would become fully awake, but unaware that anything had happened. Fortunately for Tater, proper testing eventually confirmed that he suffered from autoimmune thyroiditis, and he was prescribed a twice-daily thyroid supplement. Within six weeks, Tater's abnormal behavior had disappeared to the extent that he is now 90% rage-free.

Tater is certainly a lucky dog. He ended up in a home with someone who understood that there was more to his rage than met the eye, and who cared enough for him to follow through until a proper diagnosis and treatment was established. Had Tater's guardian not been inclined to get to the root of his behavioral issues, his life could very well have ended up cut tragically short by euthanasia, and he would have been wrongfully labeled as just another "bad" dog.

A dog's abnormal behavior can stem from a variety of medical causes, but it can also reflect underlying problems of a psychological nature. Interestingly, behavioral and psychological changes in humans have been linked to thyroid dysfunction since the 19th Century. According to one study, 66% of people with Attention Deficit-Hyperactivity Disorder (ADHD) were found to be hypothyroid. When their thyroid levels were supplemented with hormone replacement, they showed marked improvement. A similar relationship has been established between abnormal behavior and thyroid disorder in dogs.

The thyroid and canine behavior

The exact mechanism that diminishes or alters thyroid function in canine behavior is unclear. What we do know is that both animals and people with thyroid-related behavioral issues exhibit reduced metabolism and clearance of cortisol, as well as suppressed TSH output. As we've discussed, suppressed TSH output lowers the production of thyroid hormones. At the same time, constantly elevated levels of cortisol in the blood mimic the condition of being in a constant state of stress (remember that cortisol is the "stress hormone," since it is released in higher amounts in response to "fight or flight" situations).

In people, and seemingly in dogs, chronic stress causes impairment of mental function. Chronic stress in humans has been associated with depression. Major depression has been shown in imaging studies to produce changes in neural activity or amount in areas of the brain that regulate aggression as well as other behaviors. It has also been demonstrated that there is a relationship between the **dopamine** and **serotonin** pathways and thyroid hormone in the central nervous system. Dopamine and serotonin are so-called neurotransmitter molecules that serve many functions in the brain, including important roles in behavior and cognition, voluntary movement, motivation and reward, and inhibition of the prolactin production involved in lactation, sleep, mood, attention, and learning.

Behavioral signs of canine thyroid disorder

As progress continues to be made in the study of canine thyroid disorder and its wide range of physical signs, understanding of the relationship between low or abnormal thyroid function and mental health in dogs is also expanding. Until recently, the primary behavioral symptom associated with canine hypothyroidism was lethargy, and as recently as 20 years ago, there was almost no recognition of aggression-related hypothyroidism in dogs.

Today, thanks to an accumulation of experiential knowledge combined with various research and clinical studies, a wide range of behaviors have been associated with canine hypothyroidism. These signs vary depending on the age and expected behaviors attributed to the breed type of the dog in question.

Case study

Terry, a four-and-a-half-year-old, intact male Bearded Collie, experienced a seizure at three years of age. He recovered quickly and his veterinarian could find nothing abnormal on physical examination or routine blood and urine tests, so the veterinarian decided to wait and see if further seizures occurred. Terry's behavior, however, started to become noticeably more unpredictable. He would curl his lip, growl threateningly, and bark when he didn't want to do as told. This behavior could be triggered during grooming and bathing or when he refused to come when called. While he was easily excitable and hyperactive, he had never bitten anyone. Terry appeared otherwise healthy, and had a very good diet and plenty of exercise. Although he had tried to chase and attack sheep at herding trials, he was very friendly with cats, people, and small children.

Terry's guardians had read about a connection between abnormal behavior and thyroid function in one of their breed club newsletters, so they took him back to his veterinarian and requested a full thyroid profile. The thyroid tests indicated a low level of three thyroid hormones, but there was no elevation of thyroid autoantibodies, which would signal autoimmune thyroiditis (which, as we know, is the heritable form of thyroid disease). The veterinarian placed him on the appropriate dose of thyroxine for his weight, to be administered twice daily.

After Terry was on the thyroxine for only one week, a miracle seemed to happen. His behavior steadily improved, he was much calmer and no longer anxious, and his aggressive tendencies had diminished. Retesting of his thyroid profile in eight weeks showed improvement in thyroid levels to match the resolution of his behavioral issues.

In puppies and young adult dogs

Our canine companions are becoming afflicted with hypothyroidism and thyroid dysfunction at an unprecedented early age. In recent years, an increasing number of sudden thyroid-related behavioral changes have been documented in dogs around the time of puberty or as young adults. Most of these dogs are purebreds or crossbreeds that originate from breeds or dog families susceptible to a variety of immune problems and allergies. Examples include the Golden Retriever, Akita, Rottweiler, Doberman Pinscher, English Springer Spaniel, Shetland Sheepdog, and German Shepherd. For most of these animals, neutering of either sex does not alter the symptoms, and in some cases the behaviors actually intensify after the dog is neutered.

Younger dogs may show minor signs of thyroid disorder before the condition deteriorates to the sudden onset of behavioral aggression. These "early warning signs" of canine thyroid dysfunction in puppies and young adults include:

- Inattentiveness
- Fearfulness
- Seasonal allergies
- Skin and coat disorders (pyoderma, allergic inhalant or **ectoparasite** (topical parasite) dermatitis, alopecia, and intense itching

37

Imagine that your quiet, sweet-natured puppy suddenly changes in personality as he enters into puberty, or shortly thereafter. Your previously well-mannered and outgoing pet (perhaps he even attended obedience classes or dog show events) now acts like a completely different dog, displaying one or more signs of abnormal behavior, including:

- Whining
- Nervousness
- Schizoid behavior
- Fear around strangers
- Hyperventilating
- Disorientation
- Failure to be attentive

Would you know what to make of these symptoms? Would you understand that there is a good possibility of an underlying physical condition? Would you think to have your dog tested for thyroid dysfunction?

All too often—as evidenced by the millions of animals abandoned and put to death each year—the answer is "no."

In adult dogs

The most common behavioral signs of hypothyroidism in adult dogs are:

- Aggression (unprovoked towards other animals and/or people)
- Seizures (sudden onset in adulthood)
- Disorientation
- Moodiness
- Erratic temperament
- Hyperactivity
- Hypoattentiveness
- Depression
- Fearfulness and phobias
- Anxiety
- Submissiveness
- Passivity
- Compulsiveness
- Irritability

After emerging from one of these episodes, most dogs behave as though they are coming out of a trance-like state, and are unaware of their previous behavior.

In a large collaborative study between one of the authors (WJD) and Drs. Nicholas Dodman and Linda Aronson of the Tufts University School of Veterinary Medicine, the major categories of aberrant behaviors identified were aggression (40% of cases), seizures (30%), fearfulness (9%), and hyperactivity (7%). Some dogs exhibited more than one of these behaviors. Within these four categories, thyroid dysfunction was found in 62% of the aggressive dogs, 77% of seizuring dogs, 47% of fearful dogs, and 31% of hyperactive dogs.

This study showed that dogs with aberrant aggression responded favorably to thyroid replacement therapy within the first week of treatment. In some cases, if only a single dose was missed, the dogs quickly resumed their previous behavior problems.

For some dogs, the first behavioral signs of a thyroid condition are sudden seizures or seizure-like disorders (tremors, twitching of face or body muscles, restless pacing or anxiety, star gazing, and fly snapping) that occur at any time from puberty to midlife. In such cases, the dog appears perfectly healthy outwardly, but suddenly seizures occur or the dog acts bizarrely for no apparent reason. The seizures or episodes are often spaced several weeks to months apart, may coincide with the full moon, and can appear in brief clusters. In other cases, a dog can become aggressive and attack those around him shortly before or after having one of the seizures or episodes. The numbers of dogs showing these various types of aberrant behavior appear to be increasing in frequency over the last decade.

Case study
Rocky, a two-year-old, intact male Golden Retriever, suffered from **cluster seizures** (two or more seizures occurring within minutes or hours of each other in between which the animal regains consciousness). Thyroid testing revealed that Rocky's **thyroglobulin autoantibody (TgAA)** level was elevated (elevated TgAA are typically present in the serum of dogs with autoimmune thyroiditis), although his basal thyroid levels were normal. When Rocky's guardians started him on a raw food diet, his conventional veterinarian refused to treat his seizures unless his diet was switched back to commercial pet food. Fortunately for Rocky, his "mom" and "dad" took matters into their own hands, rather than yielding to the pressure from their veterinarian. They contacted a holistic veterinarian, who prescribed thyroxine and phenobarbital, and supported their choice to feed Rocky a raw diet. As of the date of this writing, Rocky remains seizure-free.

Dogs most susceptible to thyroid-related behavioral issues
The age at which behavioral symptoms of canine thyroid dysfunction begin to manifest can vary widely—from as young as six months to as old as 15 years.

THE CANINE THYROID EPIDEMIC

Spayed females and neutered males are at higher risk than their sexually intact counterparts. This is likely because of the sex hormonal pathways that influence behavior
through the hypothalamus portion of the brain. In addition, mid-sized to large breeds
are more often affected and purebreds are much more susceptible than mixed breeds.

Some of the most susceptible breeds for developing thyroid-related behavioral problems are (listed in order of frequency):

- Golden Retriever
- Akita
- Rottweiler
- Doberman Pinscher
- English Springer Spaniel
- Shetland Sheepdog
- Small Terrier breeds
- German Shepherd

However, any breed or mixed breed can be afflicted with a set of behavioral issues
when thyroid function is altered metabolically.

Approximately 95% of dogs with thyroid-related behavioral issues are afflicted with
primary hypothyroidism (hypothyroidism that is a direct result of thyroid disorder)
rather than another condition that affects thyroid function—i.e., a non-thyroidal illness. About 60-90% of dogs with primary hypothyroidism suffer from lymphocytic
thyroiditis, the autoimmune (heritable) form of hypothyroidism.

Treating dogs with thyroid-related behavior problems

Studies assessing the benefits of thyroid replacement therapy to treat related behavioral issues are very promising. Results with the standard twice-daily supplementation
of thyroid replacement were evaluated in 95 cases, with 61% of dogs showing significant behavioral improvement. Of these animals, 58 dogs displayed greater than 50%
improvement in their behavior and another 23 dogs had greater than 25% but less
than 50% improvement. Only 10 dogs experienced no appreciable change, and two
dogs had a worsening of their behavior.

These results are amazing when compared to 20 cases of dominance aggression treated
with conventional behavior modification or other habit modification over the same
time period. In those instances, only 11 dogs improved more than 25%, and of the
remaining nine cases, three failed to improve, and three were euthanized or placed in
another home.

This ongoing study now includes more than 2,000 dogs brought into veterinary clinics due to aberrant behavior. Results find a significant relationship between thyroid

dysfunction and seizure disorder as well as thyroid dysfunction and dog-to-human aggression. Data on thyroid disorder and dog-to-dog aggression are also significant, but less so.

The take-away lesson here is that if your otherwise healthy dog displays sudden behavioral changes, don't automatically assume they are of a psychological nature before first exploring all possible underlying medical causes. The sudden onset of aggressive behavior or any of the other abnormal behaviors listed above warrants a trip to the veterinarian for a complete thyroid antibody profile, additional laboratory workup, and clinical evaluation, including:

- Complete medical history
- Clinical examination
- Neurological workup
- Routine laboratory testing of blood counts, blood chemistry and thyroid antibody profiles
- Urinalysis
- Fecal exam
- X-ray

Additional laboratory tests may be indicated based on the dog's specific symptoms. If all of these tests prove to be negative, evaluation by a qualified behavioral consultant should be pursued.

If the behavior is a result of hypothyroidism, your veterinarian can prescribe thyroid replacement therapy, enabling your dog to begin his journey back to physical and mental wellness.

Take home points

- Sadly, millions of dogs are abandoned and/or euthanized each year for behavioral issues that could have been managed or reversed with the proper thyroid treatment.
- Animals and people with thyroid-related behavioral issues exhibit reduced metabolism and clearance of cortisol, as well as suppressed TSH output.
- Thyroid hormone affects the dopamine and serotonin pathways in the central nervous system.
- It is only within the last couple of decades that there has been an understanding of the relationship between aggression and hypothyroidism in dogs.
- Thyroid-related behavioral changes can occur as early as puberty.
- Younger dogs and adult dogs exhibit different behavioral signs related to canine thyroid disorder.

- "Early warning signs" of canine thyroid dysfunction in puppies and young adult dogs include inattentiveness, fearfulness, seasonal allergies, and skin and coat disorders.

- Sudden seizures or seizure-like disorders could be the first behavioral signs of a thyroid condition in adult dogs.

- Symptoms of thyroid-related behavioral disorders can begin to manifest anywhere from as young as six months to as old as 15 years.

- Groups at higher risk for thyroid-related behavioral issues include purebreds, spayed females and neutered males, and mid-sized to large breeds.

- Research shows that there has been great success in using thyroid replacement therapy to treat related behavioral issues.

- If your dog exhibits sudden behavioral changes, don't assume they are of a psychological nature. Be sure to take him to your veterinarian for a complete thyroid workup and evaluation.

- If your dog's aberrant behavior is due to hypothyroidism, thyroid hormone treatment will get him back on his four feet and feeling better in no time.

CHAPTER 4

How do I Know if My Dog has a Thyroid Disorder?

_____

If, after reading this far, you feel like you could wow your friends at the next cocktail party with your knowledge of canine thyroid disorder, bravo! You have obviously been paying attention and by now have a solid understanding of this "epidemic." It's now time to take the next step and apply that knowledge in a way that will enable you to identify the possible warning signs in your own four-legged friend.

This chapter is all about action steps you can take that will directly enable you to compare your dog's physical and behavioral attributes over an extended period of time, providing a reference that will alert you to possible concerns. And, although this book's focus is on disorders of the thyroid, you can integrate the steps in this chapter to proactively track every aspect of your dog's health.

As you read on, you will learn how to keep a detailed "canine health journal"—a written record of your dog's physical and behavioral well-being over the course of weeks, months, and years. Sound daunting? Don't worry. If you can dedicate a half-hour per week to your dog's health, you can keep up with your journal. Remember, your dog is dependent on you for everything, including acting as his health care advocate. Your journal will serve as a valuable record as you speak out on his behalf. No longer will you have to approach your veterinarian and say, "Buddy is not acting quite right, but I can't pinpoint what's wrong" or "I read something online and I think my dog has it." With your journal, you will have concrete, substantive proof of specific health symptoms and the times and circumstances in which they occurred. Now, that's something your veterinarian can work with!

Remember, there are no "quick fixes" or shortcuts to wellness. If you were motivated and interested enough in your dog's health to buy this book and read it this far, then we are confident that you are motivated and interested enough to jot down some notes and observations to help facilitate your dog's health throughout his lifetime.

We broke this chapter down based on special considerations for puppies, adults, and seniors, so feel free to jump to the appropriate section for your dog's life stage.

Puppies

If you're the proud parent of a puppy, congratulations! The first year of your new dog's life is a time filled with lots of fun, play, and excitement—for both of you! You're also reading this book at a particularly opportune time, since starting your canine health journal while your dog is still a youngster gives you the advantage of creating a lifelong record that will help both you and your veterinarian keep him in tip-top shape as he ages.

Characteristics of healthy puppies include:

- High level of alertness
- Bright, shiny, sparkly eyes
- Very attentive
- Full of energy (play hard, then fall sound asleep, and wake up full of energy again)
- Excellent appetite
- Highly social and interactive

Since your pup is a newcomer to your household, begin his life of wellness with a thorough veterinary exam that includes:

- Complete blood profile: CBC (Complete Blood Counts), Chem (Serum Chemistry Profile)
- Urinalysis
- Fecal test
- Physical examination
- Cardiac auscultation (listening to the heart with a stethoscope)

A comprehensive veterinary exam will establish your pup's current level of health and provide a baseline to which you can refer as he matures into adulthood and beyond.

If possible, also try to establish a "health history" via your puppy's parents and siblings. If your dog came from a breeder, ask them for the current health records of other family members. Prior to bringing your pup home, spend time watching him interacting with his littermates and parents (or at least his mother). By observing him in his "natural" environment, you will be able to recognize any significant changes in his personality that occur after you take him home. As you evaluate your pup and jot down notes in your journal, watch closely for both physical and behavioral signs that could indicate a problem. Was your little playmate sociable and interactive at the breeder's house, but huddles in a corner and appears frightened at yours? If so, something is definitely wrong.

Closely monitor both the physical characteristics and behavior of your puppy so you can recognize sudden changes as well as more subtle shifts over time. Suppose that your puppy experiences significant or chronic intermittent diarrhea. The first thing you'll need to do is determine whether this change is sudden or whether it has progressively worsened over the course of a day or more. A sudden flare-up could mean that your precocious pup has gotten into something he shouldn't have, such as the garbage or an undesirable object in the lawn or garden. Also, have you changed his food abruptly? An incident that continues for more than 24 hours, however, could signal a serious medical condition such as a blockage or underlying illness. Of course, the information you provide to your veterinarian will be quite different for each of these scenarios, and in either case you will likely be worried as you attempt to figure out what is wrong. During such times, being bombarded by questions can seem overwhelming and confusing as you strive to remember exactly what occurred. Keeping a journal provides the advantage of having a clear, concise record of your dog's symptoms that you can relay to your veterinarian.

Here is some suggested information to include in your puppy's health journal:

Appearance

- Weight
- Height and length
- Appearance of eyes, outer ear canals, teeth, feet, coat, and skin

Behavior

- Sociability
- Playfulness
- Attentiveness

Physical

- Energy level
- Frequency of urination
- Frequency and appearance of stools

Nutrition

- Type of diet
- Volume of food consumed
- Level of hunger

Adults

If you and your adult dog have a "history" together, then you are no doubt well aware of what is normal for him both physically and behaviorally. This is the time, however, to begin paying even closer attention to his day-to-day health. Give your canine companion a quick "mini physical" once a week and jot down your findings in your journal. You will soon notice that patterns develop. If a possible health concern does arise, the break in the pattern will pop out at you immediately, enabling you to address the issue in a timely manner. This written record will also prove invaluable when you discuss the health concern(s) with your veterinarian.

Weekly "mini physical" checklist

Hair. Your dog's coat should feel soft and appear full and glossy, without being oily. Pay attention to signs of excessive shedding or hair that is dull, dry, or brittle. Watch for hair that is easy to pull out or hair loss around the trunk, thighs, and tail.

Skin. Your dog's skin should be smooth and springy to the touch. There should be no scales, scabs, growths, red patches, or hyperpigmentation. Inflamed, itchy, or foul-smelling skin can signal bacterial infections such as "staph" pyoderma. Use a fine-toothed flea comb as part of your weekly "mini physical" to check for fleas, ticks, and other parasites.

Eyes. Healthy eyes are bright and shiny, with no swelling or excessive tearing. Redness around the eye and yellow or greenish discharge could indicate conjunctivitis. Cloudiness may be a sign of cataracts or glaucoma.

Ears. Healthy ears are light pink inside, and the ear canal should be free of thick wax build-up, oozing, or pus. There should be no swelling, redness, or foul odor. If your dog scratches his ears, shakes his head frequently, or rubs his ears on the carpet or furniture, he probably has an ear infection (e.g. bacterial, yeast, mites), an inhalant allergy, or food intolerance.

Teeth and gums. Since periodontal disease has been linked with more serious illness in dogs, check his teeth and gums weekly. Regular at-home oral exams will help ensure that developing problems are identified and treated before they become serious. Check for gums that are red, inflamed, or bleeding, as well as for teeth that are loose, discolored, or sensitive to the touch. Take a couple of minutes to brush your dog's teeth with a special "doggie" toothpaste or dental gel (available at pet stores or from your veterinarian) to prevent tartar build-up, or use a dental additive in his water to help control plaque formation. Bad breath and excessive drooling can also signal teeth and gum problems as well as more serious medical conditions.

Weight. If feasible, weigh your dog monthly and record the weight in your journal. Loss of weight could be a sign of gastrointestinal disease, kidney disease, liver disease, heart disease, dental disease, or cancer. Weight gain could indicate medical conditions such as hypothyroidism and Cushing's disease, or that you are overfeeding him.

Urine. Monitor the frequency and amount of your dog's urine. Pay attention to whether he is straining to go, or shows signs of pain while urinating. If your house-broken dog suddenly begins losing control of his bladder in the house, have him examined for a medical condition such as a urinary tract infection or kidney disease, or an enlarged prostate in an intact male. The color of the urine is also important. Normal urine should appear clear yellow. A pink or darker red tint indicates blood, which could result from a variety of conditions such as urinary tract infections, bladder or kidney stones, **pyometra** (a potentially fatal uterine infection in intact female dogs—see below), or certain cancers of the urinary or reproductive system.

Stool. Normal stools are small, brown, and firm. However, your dog should not have to strain to eliminate. A dry, hard stool could indicate a nutritional or health problem. Diarrhea should also be closely monitored. Diarrhea can result from simple stomach upset such as from eating something disagreeable, or it can indicate a more serious condition. Diarrhea that persists for more than 24 hours or is accompanied by other symptoms, such as vomiting or blood in the stool, warrants prompt veterinary attention.

Loss of appetite (anorexia). A dog's reluctance or refusal to eat for a day or more could result from something as simple as a dislike for a new food, but it could also indicate a health issue with the teeth, gums, mouth, or stomach (e.g. gastritis), or a more serious internal problem. Never brush off your dog's loss of appetite as "he's just being finicky." Many internal illnesses can cause a dog to stop eating, including gastrointestinal disease and bloat, kidney disease, infections, neurological disease, autoimmune disease, cardiovascular disease, blood, skin, or brain disease, cancer, and diseases of other organs. Loss of appetite can also result from an intestinal mass or blockage from eating foreign objects or material or any illness that causes pain. An overactive bowel (increased intestinal peristalsis) can also telescope on itself (intussusception) causing a potentially fatal perforation. If your dog refuses to eat, bring him in promptly for a thorough veterinary examination.

Excessive thirst (polydipsia). Increased thirst can signal any one of several medical conditions, including diabetes mellitus and diabetes insipidus, Cushing's disease, kidney disease, and liver disease. It can also be emotional (psychogenic).

Lethargy (lack of energy). If a normally enthusiastic and energetic dog suddenly appears listless, fatigued, or has lost interest in the activities he used to enjoy, this could signal a serious illness or stress. Lethargy can result from hormonal disorders such as hypothyroidism. It can also indicate a severe life-threatening condition such as cancer, infection, heart disease, immune disease, or physical trauma. Grief can also manifest this way, as a form of depression, from loss of a human or pet companion. If your dog is lethargic for more than a day, take him to his veterinarian for a complete examination.

Reproductive health (for intact females):

- **Heat cycle.** It's very important to write down when the dog comes into heat, note the amount and color of the vaginal discharge, length of the cycle, and anything unusual in the expected pattern from her prior heats.

- **Pseudo-pregnancy** (false pregnancy). Signs of pseudo-pregnancy include nesting, reduced appetite, weight gain, mammary enlargement, and lactation (milk production) from six-to-12 weeks after the onset of estrus. Spaying is the only permanent treatment for recurrent false pregnancy.

- **Pyometra.** Pyometra is a serious uterine infection where the uterus fills with pus (pyometra literally means "pus in the uterus."). It usually occurs 60-90 days after the onset of a heat cycle. There are two types of pyometra: open and closed. With open pyometra, the pus is released from the body via the vagina. This creates a blood-tinged or **purulent** (pussy), foul vaginal discharge that drains from the infected uterus. Closed pyometra is often more serious, as the pus is not discharged through the vagina, but rather accumulates in the uterus. Since there is no vaginal discharge, pet parents can easily miss the signs of closed pyometra, which include anorexia, malaise, fever, and slight bloating of the abdomen. With closed pyometra, bacteria enter the blood stream and overwhelm the immune system, causing systemic (whole body) illness, potential organ failure, and possible death. The only conventional treatment for pyometra is spaying. Removing the infected uterus both cures the existing pyometra and prevents any future risk of infection.

- **Lactation.** See "pseudo-pregnancy" above.

As we've mentioned, dogs who are used for breeding must be tested for thyroid and other genetic disorders to avoid passing these heritable conditions along to their offspring. Dogs that test positive for any established genetic disorder should not be used for breeding.

Case study

Terri, a five-and-a-half-year-old, intact female Newfoundland, had a history of recurrent pseudo-pregnancies since her maiden heat cycle. Even so, she had successfully carried and whelped a litter of eight pups when she was three years old. Terri's owners had wanted her to have a second litter, but she failed to conceive after three tries. Since they had decided that her upcoming heat would be the last try, they took her to a veterinary reproduction specialist. The specialist advised that she come in for a thorough checkup during her next anestrus period (12-16 weeks after the onset of her prior estrus, when her body would be sex-hormonally quiescent, and she had finished her signs of false pregnancy). The checkup would include a review of her personal and family history, a physical examination, blood and urine tests, an anterior vaginal culture taken at the entrance to the uterus, and a vaginal examination.

The blood and urine tests were normal, except for high cholesterol and apparent hypothyroidism. However, since Terri's thyroid autoantibodies were not elevated, her hypothyroidism was not determined to be of the clearly heritable kind. Of course, her reproductive issues and hypothyroidism would still have likely run in her family and could also appear in some of her offspring. A review of Terri's family background confirmed these predispositions.

The vaginal culture grew two bacteria commonly encountered in cases of false pregnancy and infertility—Escherichia coli (E. coli) and beta-hemolytic Streptococcus (B-Strep). Terri was treated back-to-back for 14 days each with the appropriate antibiotics identified from the bacterial culture and sensitivity performed.

*Note: When performing vaginal cultures, two points are important to obtain clinically relevant results: 1) An intact female should be in **anestrus** (in between heats) to avoid culturing the bacteria—including non-pathogenic mycoplasmas or urea plasmas—that normally frequent the external vagina during other times of the heat cycle; and 2) The culture should be taken with a guarded (sleeved) sterile culturette from the anterior vagina at the opening to the uterus.*

Based on thinking first and foremost about Terri's health, her guardians decided to just treat her hypothyroidism and not to try to breed her again. After several months of thyroid hormone replacement therapy and completing another heat cycle uneventfully (without any pseudo-pregnancy) Terri was spayed. This was performed during the anestrus period following her normal estrus.

These were responsible breeders thinking first and foremost of Terri's health, and not wishing to produce more puppies that could carry her genetic predispositions. They also informed the people who purchased puppies from Terri's first litter to watch for signs of hypothyroidism and infertility. Bravo!

Special considerations for adopted adult dogs
Did your furry companion arrive into your family a bit later in life? No problem. Take him to his veterinarian for a complete physical examination and wellness profile to serve as the baseline for your canine health journal. Also, pay special attention to his behavioral habits for the first few months and write them down in your journal. This will help you to become familiar with your new dog's normal behavior patterns so you can spot any future changes.

Seniors
The age at which a dog is considered a "senior" varies according to the size of the breed:

- Giant breeds = 8 years or older
- Medium sized breeds = 9 or 10 years
- Small breeds = 10 years or older

As dogs age, they experience normal physiological and behavioral changes. Older dogs, similar to elderly people, may develop Canine Cognitive Dysfunction (discussed below). If your dog has entered his geriatric years, you've more than likely noticed that he's "slowing down" or that he's lost interest in many of the activities he once enjoyed. Other signs of "old age" also might have set in, such as disorientation, social withdrawal, hearing loss, blindness, weakness, exercise intolerance, and reduced appetite or behavioral changes such as those discussed below. But, it's no big deal, right? After all, these are normal symptoms of a dog that's growing older. Not necessarily.

It's true that many of the changes you notice in your dog may be attributed to his getting on in years. However, many symptoms that pet parents dismiss as a normal part of the aging process are actually signs of serious illness. For this reason, regular veterinary check-ups are more important now than at any other time in your dog's life. Your senior dog should visit his veterinarian at least once a year for a complete wellness exam—more often if particular health concerns arise.

The importance of regular check-ups in senior dogs is well documented. A 1998-1999 study by VCA West Los Angeles Animal Hospital and Antech Diagnostics showed that a significant number of apparently healthy geriatric dogs and cats actually had serious health issues such as renal insufficiency, liver dysfunction, adrenal hyperactivity or hypothyroidism (dogs), and hyperthyroidism (cats). Importantly, they did not yet display obvious clinical signs of illness and would never have been diagnosed had it not been for a routine physical examination. If you have any doubts about whether your dog's symptoms are due to "normal aging," it's best to err on the side of caution and let your veterinarian make the determination.

Senior dogs do not have the same stamina levels or resilient immune systems as younger dogs, so catching illness early is crucial. The sooner you diagnose a health issue, the sooner you can make the necessary adjustments to your pet's diet and administer the proper treatment. Early diagnosis is critical to ensuring the illness does not rapidly progress to the point where it is too late to effectively manage.

Tracking your dog's health in a journal is especially important as he ages, since you will be able to monitor patterns of change that can indicate a serious medical condition and address it earlier rather than later. Just as we discussed in the section on adult dogs, it's a good idea to take a few minutes each week to give your senior dog a "mini physical." Pay special attention to the following:

Weight. If feasible, weigh your dog at least once a month. Unexplained weight loss is a possible sign of serious illness, including gastrointestinal disease, kidney or liver disease, heart disease, dental disease, bone and joint disease, and cancer. Weight gain could indicate medical conditions such as hypothyroidism and Cushing's disease, arthritis, and exercise intolerance from heart disease or overfeeding.

Skin and coat. It's normal for a dog's hair to become grey as he ages, especially around the muzzle. Other changes in the coat, such as thinning or excessive shedding, however, could be a sign of illness and should be checked by a veterinarian. Groom your dog regularly and check for lumps, bumps, or any other suspicious signs on the skin. Although these could indicate benign tumors or fatty deposits, cancerous tumors are also possible. Be sure to have any abnormal lumps or bumps examined by your veterinarian.

Eyes/vision. Look into your dog's eyes. Are they bright and shiny? A bluish-grey haze in the center of the lenses could point to nuclear sclerosis, a common age-related change that begins to affect dogs at about seven years old. The good news is that nuclear sclerosis does not noticeably impact a dog's vision. However, cloudy eyes could also indicate more serious conditions such as cataracts or glaucoma. Pay close attention to signs of vision loss. Is your canine companion walking into walls or having trouble seeing you when you call him? Your veterinarian will be able to perform an ophthalmic exam to pinpoint the problem and determine the proper course of treatment.

Teeth/gums. Providing good home dental care is important throughout your dog's life, since dental disease is linked to serious illness. Brush your dog's teeth regularly with toothpaste or gel made especially for dogs, and check the inside of his mouth for signs of trouble. Red, swollen, or bleeding gums all indicate oral disease. Bad breath is not "normal" for older dogs, and can indicate serious health problems, such as an oral abscess, infections, cancer, or even kidney disease.

Urination/defecation. Is your senior dog suddenly having accidents in the house? If so, his incontinence could indicate a serious health problem. Increased urination is a symptom of a variety of medical conditions, including Cushing's disease, pyometra, diabetes mellitus, diabetes insipidus, liver disease, kidney disease, intervertebral disc disease, prostatic hypertrophy, and bladder or kidney stones. Pay attention to whether your canine companion strains to go, or if he shows signs of pain while urinating or defecating. Monitor the frequency, amount, and color of your dog's urine and stool. Report any signs of concern immediately to your veterinarian.

Excessive thirst. Increased thirst often goes hand-in-hand with increased urination and can signal any one of several medical conditions, including diabetes mellitus, diabetes insipidus, Cushing's disease, kidney disease, and liver disease.

Vomiting. Recurrent or persistent vomiting up food or bile in an older dog can signal gastritis or a more serious upper gastrointestinal tract problem. This warrants a prompt veterinary examination.

Stool. Constipation or diarrhea in an older dog should be closely monitored. Diarrhea that persists for more than 24 hours or is accompanied by other symptoms, such as vomiting or blood in the stool, indicates the need for prompt veterinary attention.

Loss of appetite (anorexia). Loss of interest in eating warrants a trip to the vet, as it can indicate medical issues such as diabetes mellitus, liver disease, kidney disease, gastrointestinal disease, gastritis, foreign body, Cushing's disease, dental disease, stress, pain, and cancer.

Activity level/mobility. Just as older people show normal signs of "slowing down" as they age, so do dogs. Your pet may sleep more, tire more easily after exercise, and have a harder time with activities requiring mobility, such as climbing stairs. Even so, it's important to keep a close watch for the difference between what is "normal" and what could indicate a medical problem. If your dog whines when standing up or changes his gait when walking, he may be suffering from the pain of severe arthritis or intervertebral disc disease. Lethargy and weakness are signs of possible medical conditions including heart disease, anemia, diabetes mellitus, hypothyroidism, and cancer. If you're unsure of whether your dog's change in activity level or mobility is typical of an aging dog or could indicate cause for concern, it's better to be safe than sorry and take him for a thorough examination.

Behavioral changes. Many senior dogs experience a form of senile dementia known as **Canine Cognitive Dysfunction (CCD)**. CCD, which is very similar to Alzheimer's disease in humans, results from chemical and physiological changes that occur in the brains of older dogs. Like Alzheimer's, CCD is progressive and irreversible. Clinical signs of CCD include:

- Incontinence
- Confusion/disorientation in familiar surroundings
- Increased sleeping/insomnia
- Loss of interest in people and events
- Forgetfulness of housetraining habits
- Failure to recognize familiar people and animals
- Wandering aimlessly/pacing
- Loss of appetite/forgetting to eat
- Staring into space
- Decreased activity level
- Lack of response to name/commands
- Failure to pay attention

If your dog shows signs of CCD, an examination by his veterinarian can confirm a diagnosis and rule out any other possible age-related behavioral conditions. Many dogs with age-related cognitive dysfunction respond to treatment with deprenyl (brand name Anipryl™), which is also approved by the FDA for age-related urinary incontinence (a common symptom of CCD). Other alternative and complementary therapies can also help.

Dogs also experience age-related behavioral changes that are not related to CCD, such as aggression, anxiety, sudden lack of sociability, and nervousness. These abnormal behaviors may be due to changes in their environment, or they may result from an underlying medical condition such as hypothyroidism or the pain of arthritis or intervertebral disc disease.

If you notice behavioral changes in your dog, examine your family dynamics to determine if it could be contributing to his issues. The introduction of a new animal, the birth of a child, or the return of a family member who has been away for a while can all produce stress in older animals who are no longer as capable of adapting to new situations. Remember, animals are like "sponges" that absorb the energy and emotions of their environments and their human families. Changes in family dynamics or sudden strife can profoundly impact your dog's emotional well-being and behavior.

Only your veterinarian is qualified to determine whether your dog's abnormal behavior is emotional or related to a medical condition. However, don't dismiss behavioral changes without having them checked out. If they are the result of hypothyroidism, your veterinarian can prescribe hormone replacement therapy that will enable your canine companion to feel better in no time.

Special considerations for adopted senior dogs

Have you opened your home and your heart to a senior dog? If so, congratulations! Older dogs have so much love to give. However, unless the dog spent his younger years with a relative or friend, you may not have any medical records or knowledge to serve as a reference of past health issues. In fact, his current medical condition may very well be a mystery. Take your older buddy to the veterinarian for a complete wellness exam as soon as possible. This will enable you to create a baseline for future reference, as well as to discover any issues that require immediate medical treatment.

Whether you've just welcomed a new puppy into your life, adopted an adult dog, or are caring for your faithful companion through his senior years, monitoring your pet's health and recording your observations in a canine health journal are crucial to ensure that no medical condition goes overlooked, no illness goes undiagnosed, and no treatable condition goes unattended.

You hang out with your dog on a day-to-day basis, whereas your veterinarian may see him only once a year. This puts you in a much better position to notice issues that have developed gradually over time. And, if your memory becomes cloudy and you find yourself asking, "Did Buddy *always* bark at the mailman or family members?" your journal will provide you with an irrefutable record to which you can refer.

Has your car ever made a "funny" noise that miraculously disappeared every time you took it to the mechanic? This same scenario can happen with your dog. When he's at the veterinary clinic in the confined space of an exam room, he will respond quite differently than he does at home. Nervousness, anxiety, or even curiosity can set in and alter his behavior to the point where the veterinarian does not notice the issue at hand. Enter your trusty canine health journal. If you've been recording your dog's symptoms faithfully, you can share this written history with your veterinarian as proof that his condition is indeed *not* in your imagination!

If possible, include photographs or a video as part of your canine health journal. It's true that a picture's worth a thousand words, and the best way you can demonstrate to your veterinarian that there's something wrong with your dog's mobility, behavior, or any other aspect of his health is to capture it in a photo or video. Thanks to inexpensive, miniature video cameras and cell phones, providing a pictorial health record is now possible and easy.

Including photographs as part of an animal's medical chart is gaining in popularity within the veterinary community. Many practitioners who keep detailed office notes are snapping photos of their patients as part of their records. Photos are helpful because they provide the veterinarian with a reference of any changes in the dog's general physical appearance over time. This is particularly important if the dog hasn't received a checkup for a couple of years.

So many of the symptoms we've discussed in this chapter could indicate a thyroid problem. They could also point to many other diseases and disorders that require veterinary attention. Your journal will provide important clues to help your veterinarian pinpoint the culprit in the quickest and most direct manner, eliminating unnecessary tests that take time, cost money, and cause needless discomfort for your beloved companion.

Take home points

- A "canine health journal" is your most important tool to track changes in your dog's physical and behavioral habits over time.

- New puppy parents should begin their dog's health journal immediately, as this will serve as an important reference throughout his entire life.

- Take a few minutes each week to give your dog a "mini physical" and record the observations in your journal. This will help you uncover any patterns of change in your dog's health.

- Start a health journal for your adopted adult dog right away. To establish baseline values as a comparison, take him to his veterinarian for a complete wellness examination as soon as possible.

- When issues of concern do arise, write down the information as specifically as possible (times, dates, circumstances, etc.) in your journal. If feasible, include photographs and/or video. This will help your veterinarian to make an accurate diagnosis.

- All too often, pet parents dismiss symptoms of serious illness in their older dogs as a normal part of the aging process. This is why veterinary checkups are more important now than at any other time in your dog's life.

- Senior dogs should receive a minimum of an annual wellness exam to ensure that any medical conditions are caught early.

- Whether you are looking for signs of hypothyroidism or any other condition, recording your observations in a journal is the most accurate way to get a "big picture" of your dog's health over time.

CHAPTER 5

Is My Dog at Risk?

How do you know if your dog is at risk for canine thyroid disorder? Look at him and ask yourself this very important question: "Is he a dog?" Then, he's at risk!

A strong immune system is vital to your dog's health. The immune system protects the body from foreign **antigens** (proteins) such as bacteria, viruses, parasites, fungus, and even tumor cells. When the immune system identifies an antigen, it produces antibodies that bind to it, initiating a complex process that destroys the invader. As discussed in Chapter 2 and shown in Figure 3, immune-mediated diseases such as autoimmune thyroiditis wreak havoc on the immune system, "tricking" it into attacking itself. A weakened immune system is unable to properly protect the body from the barrage of harmful intruders that inhabit our world.

The result? Dogs afflicted with autoimmune thyroiditis are susceptible to a host of medical complications and potentially life-threatening infections and diseases because of weakened immune systems. This is why it is so important to properly diagnose and treat thyroid disorders. But it's not just immune-mediated diseases that contribute to immunological dysfunction. Lifestyle factors such as stress, poor nutrition, and exposure to toxins also weaken the body's natural immune defenses.

Consider how your own lifestyle choices affect your health. When you eat poorly, work (or play) too hard, or let stress get the better of you, chances are you feel "run down," and this is often when you find yourself succumbing to illness. But, did you realize that your dog's lifestyle choices (or, more accurately, the lifestyle choices you make for him) also greatly influence his ability to fight off foreign antigens?

The good news is that we can make choices that strengthen our dogs' immune systems, rather than further weakening them. While this is important for all dogs, it's especially critical for those afflicted with an autoimmune condition. Since these dogs already suffer from generalized metabolic imbalance and often have associated immunological dysfunction, exposure to unnecessary drugs, vaccines, chemicals, environmental toxins, and improper or imbalanced nutrition can be the "last straw" that topples their already fragile immune defense mechanisms.

Let's take a look at some of the lifestyle factors that can weaken your dog's immune system, and discuss what you can do to minimize or eliminate exposure to these hazards.

It's a risky world out there

From the wide array of toxic household cleaners that occupy most of our cupboards to the pesticides saturating our lawns and the chemical flea and tick preventives we apply onto their skin, our pets' bodies are constantly bombarded by threats to their immune systems.

A healthy dog's immune system is designed to recognize and neutralize these threats throughout his lifetime. A puppy is born with a relatively small amount of immune recognition ability that is passed to him from his mother's placenta and **colostrum,** breast milk produced within the first thirty-six hours after birth. This immune recognition enables the puppy to enter the world with some ability to protect himself. For the most part, however, his immune system is still undeveloped and "naïve" to the vast array of pathogens awaiting him.

As the puppy grows up and he is exposed to more and more antigens, foreign substances, when introduced into the body, are capable of producing an immune response. As this occurs, his immune system adds these new substances to its "immune memory." This concept of immune memory explains why, for example, a dog who is allergic to wheat will still react to the wheat even years after not having been exposed to it. His immune memory cells identified wheat as a threat early in his life, and the next time he comes into contact with it, these cells still recognize it as a harmful substance. The concept of immune recognition also holds true for humans, of course.

As the dog ages and the number of antigens he is exposed to increases, his immune system must work more diligently and interactively to recognize and fight them. In this case, the immune system can be compared to a wall, with the immune memory cells functioning as the wall's building blocks. With each new antigen exposure, another building block is added to the wall to strengthen its protective abilities. Eventually, these building blocks pile up and the immune system "wall" becomes too high and unstable, causing it to collapse. This is known as the "Humpty Dumpty" effect, for obvious reasons!

Protecting our dogs' immune systems from becoming overwhelmed and eventually "toppling over" is a two-fold process. First, we must reduce or eliminate their exposure to as many reactive substances as possible. Second, we must take steps to fortify their immune systems, primarily with proper nutrition and appropriate supplementation.

Let's begin by looking at some of the risk factors our dogs face, and what we can do to reduce or eliminate them.

Environmental toxins

Many of the products we use around our homes, lawns, cars, and even on our bodies can pose a health risk to pets that walk on them, lick them, chew them, and even possibly eat them. This is especially true for those pets living with an already compromised immune system.

Common environmental toxins include:

- Lawn and garden products (fertilizers, weed killers, lawn care, swimming pool products, etc.)
- Pesticides (insecticides, fungicides, herbicides, etc.)
- Household cleaners (chemical cleaning products, bleach, air fresheners, carpet cleaners, etc.)
- Construction materials (drywall, insulation, paints, varnishes, adhesives, etc.)
- Automotive products (antifreeze, break fluid, lubricants, sealants, etc.)
- Batteries (especially battery fluids)
- Personal care products (antiperspirants, shampoos, hair sprays, etc.)
- Pet care products (insect repellent, cat litter, shampoos, etc.)
- Airborne pathogens (dust, pollen, mold, bacteria, viruses, etc.)
- Water-borne pathogens (bacteria, viruses, algae, parasites, chemicals, etc.)
- Land pathogens (bacteria, viruses, fungi, parasites, poisonous insects, toads, mushrooms, snakes, chemicals, etc.)

Have you ever closely read the labels of your favorite cleaning solutions or investigated the origins and possible side effects of any of those long chemical names? The government's National Institutes of Health (NIH) Web site (http://hpd.nlm.nih.gov/) contains health and safety information on a wide variety of household products, from air fresheners and floor cleaners to paints, adhesives, and laundry detergents. You might be surprised at some of the hazards posed by ingredients in products you use on a regular basis.

Today, there are many companies that offer safe alternatives to dangerous chemical cleaning products, so it is no longer necessary to bathe your home in toxins in order to make it sparkle. The same holds true for our lawns and gardens. There now are products that use safe, natural ingredients such as cedar oil to drive away pests with no harmful effects on our pets and children.

There are many steps you can take to reduce or eliminate environmental toxins in your dog's life. By using the above list as a reference, you can assess your home for risks and decide what you can do to help prevent the "Humpty Dumpty" effect from striking your canine companion. It's a lot easier than you think. Here are a few suggestions to get you started:

- Give your dog filtered or bottled water instead of tap water. Studies have identified numerous environmental toxins in tap water, ranging from lawn chemicals and cleaning products to prescription drugs. One contaminant found in tap water is perchlorate, a chemical used to manufacture fireworks, explosives, flares, and rocket propellant. Perchlorate inhibits the uptake of iodine, which is necessary for a properly functioning thyroid. Filling your dog's bowl with filtered or bottled water could help eliminate these toxins.

- Switch to non-toxic cleaning products. Safe alternatives to chemical cleaners are widely available and work surprisingly well. When in doubt, opt for household basics such as baking soda, vinegar, and alcohol-based products to do the job.

- Eliminate the use of poisonous pesticides on your lawn and garden. Try pet-safe cedar oil instead of toxic insecticides. Cedar oil is derived from cedar wood, which has been used for thousands of years as a natural insect repellent. Unlike toxic pesticides, cedar oil is safe for pets and children. Since it kills fleas as well as their eggs and larvae, it can also be used in place of chemical spot-on products.

- Purchase low VOC (volatile organic compound) paints when redecorating.

- Store any necessary toxic substances (such as antifreeze or break fluid) far out of your dog's reach, such as on high shelves or behind locked cabinet doors.

Reducing or eliminating toxins from your environment will not only benefit your canine companion, but will also help to keep you and the rest of your family safer and healthier.

Chemical flea and tick preventives

Of course we don't want our dogs to suffer the agony of annoying fleas, ticks, and other insects, nor do we relish it when they hop off our furry friend and infest our home. But many of the products used to eradicate these infiltrators—including popular monthly **spot-on flea and tick treatments,** those that come in a tube or a vial and are squeezed onto a certain spot on the body—contain toxic chemicals that in some cases can pose acute and chronic health risks to our dogs, including death.

As far back as 1989, a study by the Purdue University School of Veterinary Medicine Department of Pathobiology, published in the *Journal of Toxicology and Environmental Health,* found that dogs who received one-to-two topical pesticide applications per year experienced a 60% increased risk in bladder cancer. Dogs that were given more than two applications per year were 3.5 times more likely to develop bladder cancer. The risk was further increased in overweight or obese dogs.

Spot-on flea and tick control products continue to stir great concern as to their safety. In March 2010, The EPA announced an "Analysis and Mitigation Plan" for pet spot-on products, stating that, "The U.S. Environmental Protection Agency is pursuing a series of actions to increase the safety of spot-on pesticide products for flea and tick control for cats and dogs. Immediately, EPA will begin reviewing labels and determining which ones need stronger and clearer labeling statements. EPA will also develop more stringent testing and evaluation requirements for both existing and new products. EPA expects these steps will help prevent adverse reactions from pet spot-on products."

In particular, products containing organophosphates and carbamates pose severe health risks and should not be used on pets.

Organophosphates (OPs). Organophosphates are neurotoxins that kill insects by interfering with the transmission of nerve signals in their brains and nervous systems. According to a November 2000 report of the Natural Resources Defense Council (NRDC), "In overdoses, OPs can also kill people and pets. But even with normal use of flea-control products containing OPs, pets and children may be in danger." The seven OPs are chlorpyrifos, dichlorvos, phosmet, naled, tetrachlorvinphos, diazinon, and malathion. They are the active ingredients in numerous pet products. In the November 2000 report, the NRDC recommended that, "EPA should move immediately to ban the use of pet pesticides containing OPs."

Carbamates. Carbamates, made from carbamic acid, are closely related chemical compounds to organophosphates. Like organophosphates, carbamates are toxic to the brain and nervous system. If the product label lists atropine as an antidote to poisoning, the product most likely contains carbamates. The two major carbamates used in flea control products are carbaryl and propoxur. The NRDC strongly recommends against the use of carbamate insecticides on pets.

Pyrethrins/Pyrethroids. Pyrethrins are botanical insecticides derived from certain species of chrysanthemums. Spot-on flea and tick products containing pyrethroids have gained popularity over the last decade, as they are considered to be less acutely toxic to birds and mammals than organophosphates and carbamates. However, these insecticides carry their own potential toxicity risks. They work by penetrating the nerve system and causing paralysis and eventual death of the target pests. According to the Department of Health and Human Services Agency for Toxic Substances and Disease Registry (ATSDR), "Pyrethroids are manufactured chemicals that are very similar in structure to the pyrethrins, but are often more toxic to insects as well as to mammals, and last longer in the environment than the pyrethrins." ATSDR states that, "High levels of pyrethrins or pyrethroids can cause dizziness, headache, nausea, muscle twitching, reduced energy, changes in awareness, convulsions and loss of consciousness."

According to the EPA, pyrethrins and pyrethroids are included in more than 3,500 registered products, many of which are used in and around households, including on pets.

The concentrations of pyrethroids in many over-the-counter, spot-on pet treatment products are stronger than in any products approved by the EPA or the FDA for human and animal use. According to June 2008 and October 2009 studies published in *The Veterinary Journal,* pyrethroid application to the skin or coat of pets can potentially cause hyperexcitability, tremors, profuse salivation, and seizures.

According to a December 16, 2008 article of The Center for Public Integrity titled *Pets and Pesticides: Let's Be Careful Out There,* in the previous five years, "the EPA received a total of more than 25,000 reports of pet pesticide reactions of every sort—fatal, major, moderate, and minor—to over-the-counter pyrethroid spot-on products."

Most flea and tick problems can be avoided without the use of poisonous chemicals. Before you expose your dog to potentially dangerous toxins that can be absorbed through his skin, try the following:

- Bathe your dog frequently to control minor infestations.

- Keep your grass raked and cut short in areas your pet frequents.

- Comb your canine buddy with a special fine-tooth flea comb and check him for ticks after romps outdoors.

- Vacuum and wash your floors regularly.

- Frequently wash pet bedding in hot water.

Spot-on flea and tick treatments should only be used under the guidance and supervision of a veterinarian. Prescription products can be obtained from your veterinarian or purchased online or at a specialty pet store with a prescription. While these topical prescription products are approved by the EPA (or in the case of systemic products, by the FDA), many over-the-counter products are reviewed and graded against the same EPA safety and efficacy standards. That said, *one should always read the labels very carefully,* as other over-the-counter products sold in supermarkets and general pet supply stores have not been subjected to the same rigorous testing and should be avoided.

Pharmaceuticals

There are many valuable classes of medications—such as antibiotics to fight infection and non-steroidal anti-inflammatory drugs (NSAIDs) to help control pain—that enable our canine companions to live more comfortable, longer lives. But when it comes to prescription and non-prescription drugs for our dogs, it is a matter of balancing the risk with the reward. Every drug carries the potential for adverse reactions, and these reactions can be magnified in dogs with immune-mediated diseases. The key is to identify when medications are absolutely necessary and to use them in strict accordance with their prescription in order to maximize their benefits and minimize their potential risks.

Some commonly prescribed medications and their side-effects include:

Sulfonamides. Sulfonamide drugs are a class of antibiotic used to treat a wide range of bacterial infections. Sulfonamides are known to cause **thrombocytopenia** (low platelet count), and do so by either increasing platelet destruction or by bone marrow suppression. They also inhibit platelet function. Other documented side-effects of sulfonamides include fever, **hepatopathy** (liver damage), **neutropenia** (low neutrophil count), keratoconjunctivitis sicca (KCS) or "dry eye," **hemolytic anemia** (destruction of red blood cells), joint disease, **uveitis** (inflammation of the surface of the eye), skin and mucocutaneous lesions, **proteinuria** (protein in the urine), facial palsy, suspected **meningitis** (inflammation in the lining of the brain), hypothyroidism, **pancreatitis** (inflammation of the pancreas), facial edema, and **pneumonitis** (lung inflammation). Dogs with sulfonamide-induced liver damage have a generally poor prognosis.

With respect to hypothyroidism, sulfonamides are stated to interfere with the biosynthesis of thyroid hormones through inhibition of thyroid peroxidase, the enzyme that removes iodine molecules from the thyroid molecule. This drug effect is dependent on the drug's dose and duration, and is reversible upon withdrawing the drug.

Sulfonamides with the potential to produce these adverse effects in susceptible breeds or individuals include: deracoxib (Deramaxx™, Novartis), a nonsteroidal anti-in-flammatory drug, which is a benzenesulfonamide; potentiated sulfonamide antibiotics (trimethoprim sulfonamides such as Ditrim®, Bactrim® (Roche), Tribrissen®(Schering-Plough), TriSupra®, Septra® (GlaxoSmithKline), Sulfatrim® (Alpharma), SMP-TMZ and TMP-SMX); Primor® (Pfizer)(ormetoprim sulfonamide); and sulfonamide antimicrobials (such as Albon®, Pfizer).

In addition to sulfonamides, drugs that can affect serum concentrations of thyroid hormones in dogs include carprofen (Rimadyl®, Pfizer), corticosteroids (glucocorticoids), phenobarbital, potassium bromide, and propanalol.

Dog breeds documented to be hypersensitive to sulfonamides include Doberman Pinschers, Miniature Schnauzers, Rottweilers, Samoyeds, Weimaraners, and other white-coated breeds. Sulfonamides are also not recommended for breeds such as the Cavalier King Charles Spaniel and English Toy Spaniel, which frequently have low platelet counts or large platelets.

Antibiotics (other than sulfonamides)

There is a wide range of antibiotics used to treat our dogs, and all of them carry the risk of adverse effects. Some common antibiotics and potential side effects include:

- **Aminoglycosides** (such as amikacin, gentamycin, streptomycin and neomycin). Reactions include kidney damage, hearing loss, facial swelling, and nerve damage.

- **Cephalosporins**. Can cause allergic reactions and gastrointestinal issues, including stomach upset and diarrhea.

- **Clindamycin.** The most common side-effect is gastrointestinal upset.

- **Enrofloxacin** (Baytril®, Bayer). Not advisable for young growing dogs as it can cause cartilage damage, urine crystals can form, and bowel upsets can occur.

- **Erythromycin.** Side-effects include liver damage, low white blood cell counts, vomiting and diarrhea, neurological problems, and blood in urine.

- **Metronidazole.** The most common adverse effects occur with overdosage and exhibit as lack of coordination and other neurological problems, low white blood cell counts, liver damage, blood in urine, and bowel upset with vomiting and diarrhea.

- **Penicillins**. Allergic reactions typically include fever and a rash, but also can show anemia, low white blood cell counts and bowel issues.

- **Tetracyclines.** One common side-effect is discoloration of teeth, especially in puppies during teething. Other issues include bowel upset, kidney and liver damage, loss of hair, and photosensitivity (sensitivity to light)

Non-steroidal anti-inflammatory drugs (NSAIDs)

NSAIDs play an important role in helping dogs cope with pain—from those who have just undergone surgery to those afflicted with stiffness, swelling, and pain associated with degenerative joint diseases such as arthritis. However, if given improperly or in excess—or to dogs of breeds or families known to react adversely to this class of drugs—these medications can cause a host of undesirable side-effects. Possible side-effects include mild reactions such as vomiting, loss of appetite, dry eye, depression, lethargy, and diarrhea to serious reactions such as gastrointestinal bleeding, ulcers, perforations, kidney, and especially liver damage, and even death. NSAIDs approved for use in animals include Deramaxx™ (Novartis) (deracoxib, also a sulfonamide—see page 62), Etogesic® (Fort Dodge) (etodolac), Metacam® (Boehringer Ingelheim) (meloxicam), Novox™ (Vedco) (carprofen), Previcox® (Merial) (firocoxib), Rimadyl® (Pfizer) (carprofen), and Zubrin® (Intervet Schering-Plough) (tepoxalin).

A key to decreasing the adverse side-effects of NSAIDs is to limit their use to short periods when they are absolutely necessary, rather than administering them on a continual long-term basis. Even for chronic conditions such as arthritis, dog parents can discuss with their veterinarians using the drug only during times when their dog's symptoms warrant strong medication. Tramadol (Ultram®, Ortho McNeil) is a safe alternative for short-term or periodic pain. For long-term use, some alternatives include DLPA (D, L phenylalanine), the essential amino acid and endorphin stimulant that controls chronic bone and muscle pain in humans and animals. Solgar™ makes a vegetable capsule version; DPA (Dog Pain Away™, Estrella Naturals) and DGP (Dog Gone Pain™, American BioSciences), the herbal mixtures; and Mobility 2™ (a mixture of Chinese herbs for humans and animals, available from Health Concerns, Oakland, CA).

Also, as some drugs can cause harm when interacting with NSAIDs, be sure to alert your veterinarian to any other prescription or non-prescription medications, as well as herbal supplements, that your dog is taking.

Corticosteroids

Corticosteroids (hydrocortisone, prednisone, prednisolone, methylprednisolone, dexamethasone, and others) are widely used in veterinary medicine, although they do not actually cure anything. The primary function of corticosteroids is to control or suppress inflammation, such as in the case of skin allergies, asthma, inflammatory bowel disease, and herniated discs. Corticosteroids are also commonly used to control allergic reactions including seasonal allergies, food allergies, bee stings, and mold reactions. All mammals produce corticosteroids naturally in their bodies. Cortisol and sex hormones, produced in the adrenal gland, are naturally occurring steroids.

Topical steroid-containing ointments or liquids—used on the skin, or in eyes or ears—also get absorbed and can cause adverse effects. Corticosteroids affect serum concentrations of thyroid hormones in dogs. In addition, corticosteroid use runs the risk of a variety of adverse reactions over both the short and long-term, which includes increased drinking and urination, increased appetite, lethargy, gastric and intestinal ulcers, muscular weakness or atrophy, increased risk of pancreatitis, liver damage, pot-bellied look and thin skin, generalized immune suppression, and failure of the adrenal glands to function properly. Corticosteroids may also induce diabetes in some pets.

Many of the side-effects of corticosteroids mimic those of **Cushing's disease (hyper-adrenocorticism)**, a common disease seen in middle-aged dogs, especially females, and caused by an overproduction of adrenal gland steroid hormones. When the symptoms are due to the use of cortisol-containing drugs, the condition is called **iatrogenic** (induced, as opposed to natural) Cushing's disease.

Hormones

Estrogens, such as diethylstilbestrol (DES) are often prescribed weekly to control urinary incontinence, but alternatives such as phenylpropanolamine (PPA) are generally safer. Estrogens can cause low platelet counts and even, on occasion, bone marrow failure.

Canine contraceptives such as mibolerone (Cheque Drops®, Upjohn) and megestrol acetate (Ovaban®, Schering-Plough) are androgenic steroids. They oppose the effects of estrogen and other hormones that cause ovulation and the subsequent production of progesterone. As these hormones are used to prevent estrus and pregnancy and are stated to be reversible, they are generally not recommended for females intended for breeding, since the next heat cycle may vary from one week to 200 days from discontinuation of the medication. They have also been used to lengthen short heat cycles and to treat false pregnancies.

If you suspect that your dog is having an adverse reaction to any drug, you should stop using it immediately and contact your veterinarian. And, of course, never give your dog a medication meant for humans unless under the guidance of your veterinarian. Many medications that adults and children take without harm—such as Ibuprofen (Advil®, Motrin®, etc.) and Naproxen (Aleve®, Anaprox®, etc.)—can be toxic for our dogs.

Case study

Maxie, a three-and-a-half-year-old, spayed parti-colored female American Cocker Spaniel, suffered from chronic ear infections and oily skin with recurrent "hot spots." She was also slightly overweight. Her veterinarian prescribed a **potentiated** (enhanced) sulfonamide antibiotic for 10 days and treated the ear infection topically with a steroid-antibiotic liquid. Previous treatment with other types of antibiotics (cephalexin and amoxicillin) had been unsuccessful. Diagnostic testing revealed that Maxie had borderline thyroid function with a low T4, but low-normal freeT4. However, it was not considered low enough to warrant therapy.

The new treatment worked very well, and after just seven days, Maxie's skin and ear infections resolved nicely. About three weeks later, however, the skin and ear infections returned with a vengeance, so Maxie's owner started her back on the sulfonamide antibiotic (which remained from the first prescription) while waiting to see her veterinarian. After just two days on the antibiotic, Maxie developed tiny purple spots on her gums, the inside of her ear flaps, and underneath her skin. This rapidly progressed to bloody diarrhea, and Maxie became very ill.

Her veterinarian diagnosed severe **thrombocytopenia** (low platelet count) and ran more blood tests, which showed significant anemia, liver enzyme elevation, and more severe hypothyroidism. A complete thyroid antibody profile confirmed autoimmune thyroiditis. Despite intensive therapy, Maxie died.

In consulting with one of the authors (WJD), the potential underlying issue was discovered to be early stage hypothyroidism from thyroiditis (which was not diagnosed initially, as thyroid autoantibodies weren't measured). The thyroiditis explained the ear, skin, and weight issues, which were aggravated by use of the potentiated sulfonamide antibiotic.

Had an accurate diagnosis been made earlier, Maxie could have been treated properly with thyroid hormone replacement therapy, which most likely would have saved her from her terrible fate.

Vaccines

A **vaccine** is a biological preparation of either modified live or killed pathogens (viruses, bacteria, or parasites) that is introduced into the body in order to promote immunity to a particular disease.

Without a doubt, modern vaccine technology has enabled us to effectively protect our dogs against serious infectious diseases. In fact, the widespread use of vaccination programs has so significantly reduced the risk of disease that today we have the luxury of questioning conventional vaccine regimens and adopting effective and safe alternatives.

There are many benefits to animal vaccines, including:

- More animal lives saved than by other medical advance
- Significantly reduced canine distemper, hepatitis, and parvovirus
- Significantly reduced feline panleukopenia
- Eliminated rabies in Europe

However, after spending many years monitoring the results, reactions, and side-effects of canine vaccines, those in the animal healthcare field now have a duty to re-examine and improve the current vaccine protocols for the safety and health of their patients.

Annual vaccine boosters: is more really better?

It's that time of year again. You open your mailbox and there it is—that postcard from your veterinarian reminding you that it's time for Buddy's annual vaccine boosters. Like a dutiful dog parent, you make the appointment and bring him in so he can receive his shots. But, have you ever wondered whether those yearly boosters are really necessary, or if they could even be harming your dog?

If your dog's annual vaccine boosters could be causing him more harm than good, then why does your veterinarian summon you back once a year (or more)? There are several possible reasons.

Many veterinary practitioners simply believe what they have been taught about vaccines in school, and they don't take the time or have the inclination to educate themselves on the latest research. They take an "if it isn't broken, then why fix it?" attitude.

Other veterinarians view canine vaccination programs as "practice management tools" rather than medical procedures. Annual vaccination has been, and remains, the single most important reason why most people bring their dogs (and cats) for an annual "wellness visit." Given the fact that these annual visits provide the bulk of many veterinarians' practices, it is not surprising that there has been significant resistance to attempts at changing the vaccination programs, despite the scientific information. This is especially true since most veterinarians believe that even if annual vaccines aren't "necessary," they certainly won't cause any harm (which is not true). This has fostered a "more is better" philosophy with regard to pet vaccines that still prevails today. However, subjecting pets to unnecessary annual boosters means that the client pays for a service that is likely to be of little benefit to the pet's existing level of protection against these infectious diseases. It also increases the risk of adverse reactions from the repeated exposure to foreign substances.

Yet another reason for the reluctance to change current vaccination programs is that many practitioners don't really understand the principles of **vaccinal immunity** (that portion of immunity conveyed by vaccines). Every animal is different and has different vaccine needs. Evidence indicates that vaccination protocols should no longer be considered a "one size fits all" program, but that each animal should be evaluated and immunized based on a program individually tailored to their needs and overall health.

Risks of over-vaccination

As we've stated, vaccines are necessary to protect our pets from infectious diseases. The key is to balance this need for protection with the risk of **vaccinosis** (adverse reactions). This is especially true for pets afflicted with immune-mediated diseases such as autoimmune thyroiditis, since over-vaccination places undue stress on the immune system and has been linked to autoimmune disease.

Side-effects from dog vaccinations can occur anywhere from instantly up to several weeks or months later. Vaccines can even cause susceptibility to chronic diseases later in a dog's life. See photos 14, 15, and 18 through 23 in the insert for some examples.

Mild reactions associated with vaccines include:

- Fever
- Malaise
- Urticaria (hives)
- Facial swelling
- Anorexia
- Vomiting
- Stiffness
- Sore joints
- Abdominal tenderness

Severe and fatal adverse events include:

- Susceptibility to infections
- Neurological disorders and encephalitis (especially seizures)
- Aberrant behavior, including unprovoked aggression
- Collapse with **autoagglutinated** (clumped) red blood cells and **icterus** (jaundice), autoimmune hemolytic anemia (AIHA) or the synonym immune-mediated haemolytic anemia (IMHA), where red blood cells are damaged and destroyed, or **petechiae** (pin-point) and **ecchymotic** (splotchy) hemorrhages from immune-mediated thrombocytopenia (ITP), when the blood platelets are destroyed. Hepatic enzymes may be markedly elevated, and liver or kidney failure may occur by itself or accompany bone marrow suppression.

There are two general types of vaccines, **MLV** (modified-live virus) and killed. As the name suggests, MLV vaccines use a modified, but weakened, form of the live virus. When the virus is injected into the body, it multiplies many-fold and stimulates the immune system's production of antibodies, creating a complete immune response that protects the body against future exposure to the disease. **Killed vaccines** use an inactivated "dead" form of the virus, along with an **adjuvant** (a substance added to a vaccine to enhance its effectiveness without itself causing an immune response). Both MLV and killed vaccines pose greater risks to dogs with autoimmune thyroiditis or other autoimmune disorders, and for epileptics. Rabies vaccines, mandated by law, often cause the most severe reactions, to the extent of being contraindicated for epileptics. A written waiver should be obtained from your veterinarian, although not all state or local authorities accept them.

MLV vaccines have been associated with the development of temporary seizures in both puppies and adult dogs who are members of breeds or crossbreeds that are susceptible to immune-mediated diseases—especially those involving hematologic or endocrine issues such as AIHA, ITP, and autoimmune thyroiditis.

In dogs with autoimmune diseases, vaccination with MLV products should be avoided as the vaccine virus being administered could potentially cause the disease. Vaccination with killed products may aggravate an already existing immune-mediated disease or prove ineffective.

In addition, **polyneuropathy**, a nerve disease that involves inflammation of several nerves, has been linked to the distemper, parvovirus, rabies and, presumably, other vaccines. Symptoms of polyneuropathy include **muscular atrophy**, wasting away of the muscle, the inhibition or interruption of neuronal control of tissue and organ function, **muscular excitation** (stimulation of muscle fibers), **incoordination** (poor muscle control or coordination), weakness, and seizures.

Additionally, vaccination of companion and research dogs with **polyvalent** or **combination vaccines**, those that contain more than one vaccine antigen, containing rabies virus or rabies vaccine alone has been found to induce production of anti-thyroglobulin autoantibodies. Since thyroglobulin is the protein precursor of the thyroid hormones T4 and T3, the body's production of anti-thyroglobulin autoantibodies can lead to the destruction of the thyroid gland. This represents an important finding with implications for the potential development of canine hypothyroidism.

Although all dogs are susceptible to vaccine-related side-effects, certain breeds are more pre-disposed to vaccinosis than others. Examples include:

- Akita
- American Cocker Spaniel
- American Eskimo Dog
- Dachshund (all varieties, but especially the long-haired)

- German Shepherd

- Golden Retriever

- Great Dane

- Irish Setter

- Kerry Blue Terrier

- Old English Sheepdog

- Poodle (all varieties, but especially the Standard Poodle)

- Scottish Terrier

- Shetland Sheepdog

- Shih Tzu

- Vizsla

- Weimaraner

Breeds with white or predominantly white coats, as well as those with coat color dilution such as fawn (Isabella) or blue Dobermans, the merle coat color, blue Yorkshire Terriers, grey Collies, harlequin Great Danes, and Australian Shepherds are also more susceptible to vaccine reactions.

If you are uncertain whether your dog's thyroid condition is the result of inherited autoimmune thyroiditis or **idiopathic thyroid atrophy** (a thyroid disorder of undetermined cause), it is wise to take a "better safe than sorry" attitude toward vaccines. By avoiding the additional assault on your dog's immune system caused by vaccines, you will be taking the necessary steps to support his overall health.

Case study

Cali, a four-year-old, intact female Cavalier King Charles Spaniel, received a reminder card in the mail that she was due for her mandated three-year rabies booster. Her other regular "core" vaccines (distemper, parvovirus, and hepatitis) were also due. Rather than automatically give Cali her other vaccines, however, her guardian elected to run serum vaccine antibody titers (see below) in order to avoid subjecting Cali to unnecessary vaccines. This was important to Cali's guardian because she was aware that the Cavalier breed was susceptible to adverse vaccine reactions. When it came to rabies, however, she knew that the law required Cali to have the booster.

Cali seemed very healthy when she went to the veterinary clinic for her rabies booster, which was given using a three-year **thimerosol** (mercury)-free vaccine. About six days after the vaccination, however, Cali seemed lethargic and was reluctant to eat. Within twenty-four hours, she could not open her mouth and screamed in pain when her owner tried to look inside her mouth. She was rushed to the veterinary clinic, where they could find nothing else wrong with her and treated her for pain and possible temporal muscle osteopathy, with a non-steroidal anti-inflammatory drug (NSAID).

Cali's guardian asked if this condition could have resulted from the rabies vaccination, but the veterinarian insisted (incorrectly, as it turned out) that this was not the case.

Later that day, Cali seemed a little brighter and could eat soft blended foods fed to her by the spoonful. The next day she was improved, but still not back to normal. A week later, after the course of therapy was completed, Cali woke up suddenly in the middle of the night with a full-blown seizure. The seizures continued every half hour or so until her guardian could get her to an emergency veterinary clinic for treatment. She was immediately sedated to stop the seizures. The next morning, upon returning to her regular veterinarian, she was started on phenobarbital.

To make matters worse, Cali had just started to come into her heat cycle. After consulting with an internal medicine specialist who referred her to one of the authors (WJD), the diagnosis of vaccinosis was made (resulting from the rabies vaccine) with the added complication of Cali's sex hormonal change from impending estrus.

Cali was treated for vaccinosis with tapering doses of corticosteroids given over four weeks. She returned to good health and then was spayed when she was in between heat cycles.

Avoid unnecessary vaccines with titer tests

If your dog suffers from an immune-mediated disorder such as autoimmune thyroiditis, has shown previous significant adverse reactions to vaccines, or has epilepsy, you can request that your veterinarian measure his serum antibody titers instead of automatically administering annual boosters. A **titer test** is a simple blood test used to check the strength of a dog's immune defenses to a disease. Except where vaccination is required by law (as applies to the rabies vaccine), all animals can have serum antibody titers measured instead of receiving annual vaccine boosters. Your veterinarian can perform titer tests annually at first and then every three years, or as necessary, thereafter. If your dog's titer levels indicate that an adequate immune memory has been established, there is little reason to create the potential for vaccinosis by introducing unnecessary antigens, adjuvants, and preservatives into his body via booster vaccines.

The cost of titering is reasonable. However, testing laboratories vary in their degree of specificity and sensitivity, so ask your veterinarian for the most sensitive titer test if your dog is at high risk for experiencing vaccinosis, or if he has already exhibited an adverse reaction to vaccines.

Be aware that some veterinarians are resistant to performing titer tests in lieu of vaccinating, as they feel that measuring an animal's serum antibody titers is not a valid way of determining his immunity to infectious diseases.

With all due respect to these professionals, this represents a misunderstanding of what has been called the "fallacy of titer testing," because research has shown that once an animal's titer stabilizes, it is likely to remain constant for many years. Properly immunized animals have sterilizing immunity that not only prevents clinical disease, but also prevents infection, and only the presence of antibody can prevent infection. As stated by the eminent expert Dr. Ronald Schultz in discussing the value of vaccine titer testing, these tests, "show that an animal with a positive test has sterilizing immunity and should be protected from infection. If that animal was vaccinated it would not respond with a significant increase in antibody titer, but may develop a hypersensitivity to vaccine components (e.g., fetal bovine serum). Furthermore, the animal doesn't need to be revaccinated and should not be revaccinated since the vaccine could cause an adverse reaction (hypersensitivity disorder). You should avoid vaccinating animals that are already protected. It is often said that the antibody level detected is 'only a snapshot in time.' That's simply not true; it is more a 'motion picture that plays for years.'"

Furthermore, protection, as indicated by a positive titer result, is not likely to suddenly drop off unless an animal develops a severe medical condition or has significant immune dysfunction. It's important to understand that viral vaccines prompt an immune response that lasts much longer than the immune response elicited by contracting the actual virus. Lack of distinction between the two kinds of responses may be why some practitioners think titers can suddenly disappear.

But not all canine vaccines produce **sterilizing immunity**, immunity that prevents further infection even when an animal is exposed. Those that do include distemper virus, adenovirus-1(hepatitis), and parvovirus. Examples of vaccines that produce non-sterile immunity are leptospirosis, bordetella, and rabies virus. While non-sterile immunity may not protect the animal from infection, it should keep the infection from progressing to severe clinical disease.

Interpreting titers correctly depends upon the disease in question. Some titers must reach a certain level to indicate immunity, but with other agents like those that produce sterile immunity, the presence of any measurable antibody indicates protection.

A positive titer test result is fairly straightforward, but a negative titer test result is more difficult to interpret. This is because a negative titer is not the same thing as a zero titer and it doesn't necessarily mean that the animal is unprotected. This is an important distinction, because for distemper and parvovirus disease, a negative or zero antibody titer indicates that the animal is not protected against canine parvovirus and may not be protected against canine distemper virus. However, a low titer may still mean that the dog is protected.

So, what does more than a decade of experience with vaccine titer testing reveal? Published studies in refereed journals show that 90-98% of dogs and cats that have been properly vaccinated develop good measurable antibody titers to the infectious agent measured. In general, serum antibody titers to the "core" vaccines along with any natural exposures last a minimum of seven-to-nine years, and likely are present for life. This corresponds with what we are seeing clinically, as the number of cases and deaths due to these diseases has decreased in the vaccinated population. So, in contrast to the concerns of some practitioners, using vaccine titer testing as a means to assess vaccine-induced protection will likely result in the animal avoiding needless and unwise booster vaccinations.

As we stress throughout this book, when it comes to your dog's health, you are his most loyal advocate. The best thing to do is trust your instincts. If you find that your veterinarian is pressuring you into overvaccinating your pet and he or she refuses to perform titer tests in lieu of yearly boosters, you can choose to walk out of the office and find a more open-minded practitioner. Your veterinarian might even try to convince you that there is no scientific evidence linking vaccinations with adverse reactions, serious illness, and even death. This is pure ignorance, and confuses well-meaning dog guardians who are searching for the facts in an effort to provide the best level of care for their canine companions.

Veterinarians are even still routinely vaccinating ill dogs as well as those with chronic diseases (such as autoimmune thyroiditis) or prior adverse vaccine reactions. This is especially problematic when it comes to rabies boosters, since many practitioners believe they are bound by law to administer the rabies vaccine, even though the product label clearly states that it is intended for healthy animals. In such cases, local authorities might accept titer tests in lieu of the rabies vaccine.

Of course, pet parents must make sure that their dogs receive the proper vaccinations in order to protect them from disease. This includes giving puppies all of their core vaccines (see Table 5-1). Of note is the fact that there have been no confirmed clinical cases of infectious canine hepatitis in North America in the last 12 years. For this reason and the fact that including the hepatitis vaccine in the "combo" vaccines given to puppies, but *not* adult dogs, suppresses tissue immunity for up to 10 days, one of the authors (WJD) excludes it from the puppy vaccination series.

However, overvaccinating in the form of unnecessary yearly boosters is not beneficial and may cause great harm by overwhelming the immune system of a sick dog, becoming the final insult that triggers an adverse reaction.

Table 5-1. "Core" Vaccines *

Dog	Cat
Distemper	Feline Parvovirus
Adenovirus	Herpesvirus
Parvovirus	Calicivirus
Rabies	Rabies

Vaccines that every dog and cat should have.

Boost your dog's immune system with proper nutrition

A wholesome, balanced diet is key to keeping your dog's immune system healthy and "toned," enabling it to do its job of resisting disease. Nutritionally-packed foods are a major component in helping the body cope with all of the negative environmental exposures it must deal with, including the chemicals and vaccines discussed above. This is particularly true for animals whose immune systems are already compromised, such as those with autoimmune thyroiditis.

Nutrients that play an important role in maintaining a healthy immune system and thyroid function include:

- Copper
- Iodine
- Linoleic acid
- Selenium
- Vitamin B-6 (pyridozine)
- Vitamin D3
- Vitamin E
- Zinc

Copper

Copper plays an important role in thyroid metabolism, especially in hormone production and absorption. Copper stimulates the production of the thyroxine hormone (T4), and prevents overabsorption of T4 in blood cells by controlling the body's calcium levels.

Copper is also required for the synthesis of **phospholipids** (lipids that contain phosphate and are a part of all cell membranes) that are found in the myelin sheaths that insulate and protect nerves. Phospholipids are required for the stimulation of TSH (Thyroid Stimulating Hormone). Thus, adequate levels are needed to prevent thyroid problems, and have been used to assist in the treatment of thyroid disease. As with any supplement, be careful of over supplementation. Too much copper can lead to copper storage disease and eventually to liver failure.

Iodine

As we discussed in Chapter 2, iodine is vital to normal thyroid function, since it is essential to the production of thyroid hormone. Given this, it's understandable that many dog parents supplement the diets of their hypothyroid canines with kelp and other foods rich in iodine in an attempt to help boost the thyroid gland. However, iodine supplementation is extremely tricky, and giving too much can prove harmful. An excess of iodine can negatively affect your dog's thyroid medication, leading to a worsening of the very hypothyroidism that you are trying to treat.

Whether or not you should supplement with iodine depends largely upon the type of diet you feed your dog. Follow these guidelines to ensure that you do not "overdose" your dog on iodine:

- If you feed your dog cereal-based kibble, do not supplement with sea kelp or other forms of iodine more than three times per week. These foods are already fortified with high doses of iodine.

- If you feed your dog a home-cooked or raw diet, you can supplement with iodine every day, taking care to follow the product guidelines.

Linoleic acid

Linoleic acid is an Omega 6 fatty acid. If you have ever supplemented your dog's diet with fish or vegetable oil to produce a healthy, shiny coat, then you have experienced the benefits of fatty acids. Fatty acids are polyunsaturated fats with specific molecular combinations of carbon, hydrogen, and oxygen. The two main groups of fatty acids are Omega 3 and Omega 6. Fatty acids that cannot be manufactured in the body, such as linoleic acid, are referred to as essential fatty acids (EFAs). EFAs must be obtained from food. Linoleic acid is the most important Omega 6 fatty acid for dogs, since it is used to produce other Omega 6 fatty acids. Linoleic acid is also especially important for the health of a dog's skin and coat, as it allows the skin to become permeable to water. Sunflower, safflower, soybean, corn, and evening primrose oil are excellent sources of linoleic acid.

Commercial pet foods often advertise themselves as "balanced," however they may contain an improper ratio of major nutrients, vitamins, and minerals. While commercial pet food manufacturers compensate for variations in ingredients by adding vitamin and mineral supplements, it is difficult to determine optimum levels for so many different breeds of animals having varying genetic backgrounds and metabolic needs. Supplementation with vitamins and minerals should not be viewed as a substitute for feeding premium quality fresh and/or commercial pet foods.

In addition, commercial foods are often highly processed and may contain chemical preservatives to enhance their stability and shelf life. These chemical preservatives detract from the wholesomeness and nutritional quality of the product.

Selenium

Selenium is another essential trace mineral with many important roles, including defending the body against oxidative damage and boosting immune response. Selenium also potentially increases the effectiveness of vitamin E. Many countries, including the United States, contain soils deficient in selenium. Crops grown on these soils—including cereal grains used for pet foods—will contain relatively low levels of selenium. Selenium is important in maintaining the health of the thyroid and a link has recently been shown between selenium deficiency and hypothyroidism. Selenium, as it relates to hypothyroidism, is often difficult to spot because blood, but not tissue, levels of thyroid hormones rise in cases of selenium deficiency. This means that although a selenium-deficient dog may display clinical signs of hypothyroidism, his blood thyroid levels will appear normal. Synthetic antioxidants still used to preserve some dog foods can impair the bioavailability of selenium (as well as vitamin A and vitamin E). To help prevent selenium deficiency, you should feed your dog a diet preserved naturally with vitamins E and C rather than with synthetic chemical antioxidants. Bear in mind, however, that selenium is also the most toxic mineral, and it is only required in very low doses.

Vitamin B-6 (pyridoxine)
Vitamin B-6 is essential for a healthy nervous system, protein metabolism, the formation and function of red blood cells, and healthy cognitive and immune function. Signs of vitamin B-6 deficiency include anemia, seizures, skin disorders, arthritis, fatigue, kidney stones, and kidney damage. Since all B vitamins are water-soluble, excess amounts are not stored in the tissues as they are with fat-soluble vitamins. If too much vitamin B-6 is ingested, it can be eliminated from the body via the urine, greatly reducing the risk of toxicity. Cooking and processing destroys much of the vitamin B-6 that's present in raw foods. Good sources of vitamin B-6 include meat, poultry, fish, whole grains, legumes, and leafy-green vegetables such as kale, collard greens, Brussels sprouts, broccoli, and chard. Bananas are also an excellent source of vitamin B-6.

Vitamin D-3
In addition to avoiding certain foods (such as too much soy) and balancing iodine intake, nutrients such as vitamin D, selenium, copper, and zinc are important to provide optimum thyroid function of healthy individuals. Vitamin D needs to be present at sufficient levels in the **nucleus** (the genetic or germ center of cells) of all cells in order for the thyroid hormone to functionally affect that cell. Vitamin D is so important that it is now called a co-hormone of thyroid function. That said, it is not a substitute for thyroid hormonal replacement in truly hypothyroid dogs. However, it can be used as a supplement *in moderation* in the vitamin D-3 form to help support thyroid metabolism. Since all commercial pet foods already contain plenty of vitamin D, be careful not to over-supplement, since this can lead to **hypercalcemia** (high blood calcium levels).

Vitamin E
Vitamin E is a fat-soluble antioxidant with many important roles for the health of our dogs. By neutralizing harmful free radicals that can cause cellular damage, vitamin E helps to prevent cancer and diseases of the circulatory system (such as arteriosclerosis), as well as slowing the aging process. Vitamin E also boosts the immune system, oxygenates the blood, improves the function of the internal organs, prevents hormones from oxidation, reduces inflammation, and helps fight infection. Vitamin E has also been used to treat skin disorders and immune-mediated diseases in dogs. Animals who are deficient in vitamin E may display "Brown Bowel Syndrome," a condition in

which their bowels ulcerate and hemorrhage and the tissue degenerates. Good sources of vitamin E include cold pressed vegetable oils, meats, nuts, seeds, and leafy-green vegetables.

Zinc

Zinc is a trace mineral essential to the health of our canine companions. Zinc is critical to the function of the entire immune system and plays a key role in more than three hundred enzymatic and metabolic processes, including cell replication and the production of thyroid hormones. It is also vital to the health of the skin. Zinc deficiency commonly results in a condition known as "zinc-responsive dermatosis," which is especially prevalent among Huskies, Malamutes, and Samoyeds—breeds that have a genetic predisposition to poor zinc absorption. Symptoms of "zinc-responsive dermatosis" include hair loss, dull and dry hair coat, scaly, crusty skin around the legs, head, and face (especially on the nose and circling the eyes, ears, chin, and mouth), poor wound healing, and thick and crusty foot pads. Zinc deficiency can also affect reproduction.

Skip the grains

Grains—and especially grains containing **gluten**, the protein component of the grain—have the potential to cause dietary sensitivities in many dogs. Grains should be avoided in animals suffering from immunologic diseases, as there is risk of an allergic reaction that can further weaken the immune system.

Wheat is the most commonly reactive grain. In fact, the Irish Setter breed has been identified as predisposed to **"wheat-sensitive enteropathy,"** a disease of the intestinal tract which results from a dietary sensitivity to gluten. Symptoms include chronic diarrhea and weight loss, or the inability to gain weight. It has not been determined which genetic attribute causes a large group of Irish Setters to be unable to tolerate wheat, but as we discussed in Chapter 1, a long history of inbreeding and line-breeding has produced breeds of very similar genetic qualities. It makes sense, therefore, that large groups of the same breed will exhibit similar dietary sensitivities. In the future, we are likely to see other breeds predisposed to certain food reactions as we continue to feed them the same offending antigens. Fortunately, "wheat-sensitive enteropathy" can be corrected by feeding a diet free of wheat and other grains that contain gluten.

Bear in mind that just because a dog food is labeled as "grain-free," this does not mean that it is also *gluten* free. Grain-free dog foods most often refer to foods that do not contain wheat, corn, and soy. However, "secondary grains" such as oats, barley, rye, millet, quinoa, and spelt that are used in the standard grain-free diets do contain gluten. If you feel your dog may have a true gluten sensitivity, it is best to eliminate all gluten-containing foods from his diet. You can then gradually reintroduce some of the less reactive grains, paying careful attention for symptoms such as vomiting (upper GI tract hypersensitivity) or diarrhea (lower GI tract hypersensitivity), excessive gas production or bloating, abdominal pain or tenderness, or constipation.

When monitoring your dog's reactivity to grains, remember that these foods do not cause an immediate acute hypersensitivity—such as the type of reaction you would see if a person who was allergic to peanuts went into anaphylactic shock from eating peanut butter. It could take as long as two-to-three days from when you feed your dog a particular grain to the time it takes his body to react.

If you are eliminating grains from your dog's diet, it's important to also refrain from offering him treats that contain grains. This might seem obvious, but many well-meaning people automatically dole out their dog's favorite treats without so much as giving a second thought to the nutritional content. This is especially true in families where children have access to the dog's treats. Fortunately, there are now many grain-free and gluten-free treat alternatives your dog will enjoy so much that he won't even miss his biscuits!

The same holds true for your dog's vitamins and minerals. Adding a vitamin/mineral supplement to his basic food is a good idea, but be careful, since many brands are either wheat or corn-based. Fortunately, many holistic pet stores and online natural pet supply sites offer a wide selection of grain-free supplements.

Even many "prescription" diets available today through veterinarians or pet specialty stores contain wheat, corn, or soy. The key is to become a good label reader and avoid these products if you feel your dog suffers from sensitivities.

Avoid other common food antigens

Grains are certainly not the only foods that commonly cause dietary reactions in dogs. The top six food antigens are:

- Wheat
- Corn
- Soy
- Milk
- Eggs
- Beef

Consider "taking inventory" of the ingredients in your dog's food to identify how many antigens it contains. If you are feeding canned or kibble, you might be surprised to find an abundance of wheat, corn, and soy ingredients listed on the labels. If this is the case, try switching to grain-free or gluten-free products and monitor your dog for any changes in his overall health.

Similarly, if beef is a staple of your dog's diet, you might try experimenting with fish, chicken, or grass-fed lamb, or even with more exotic meats such as venison, buffalo, or rabbit, which are usually better tolerated. Pork, turkey, and duck are other commonly used options.

Make sure they eat their veggies (and fruits!)

Most of us have been told our whole lives to "eat our veggies," but did you realize that munching on a nutritious array of healthy vegetables is also beneficial to your dog? Our dogs benefit from the disease-fighting nutrients in veggies just as we do. This is especially true of leafy-green and yellow-orange vegetables, which contain a wealth of important nutrients.

Leafy-green vegetables are packed with antioxidants and cancer-fighting nutrients such as **phytochemicals**, non-nutritive plant chemicals that may help prevent disease, including carotenoids (e.g.—beta-carotene, lutein, zeaxanthin), flavanoids (e.g.— quercetin, resveratrol, rutin), and phytosterols. Leafy-green vegetables are also low in fat and calories and high in fiber, so your canine companion can boost his immune system without packing on the pounds.

There are many tasty varieties of leafy-green vegetables to entice even the most carnivorous canine. Try lightly steaming or blending (to break down the fiber and cellulose) some spinach, broccoli, kale, lettuce, Italian parsley, Swiss chard, collards, bok choy, or turnip greens and offer them as part of your dog's dinner at least three times per week. You can even buy these veggies already chopped up or frozen for added convenience.

The stars of the yellow-orange family of veggies are the **carotenoids**, phytochemicals which give them their lovely bright color. Yellow-orange veggies also contain a wide variety of phytochemicals in addition to the carotenoids, including vitamin C and flavanoids, known for their antioxidant and disease-fighting properties. Have fun integrating a wide variety of yellow-orange vegetables such as squashes, carrots, pumpkin, yellow beets, yams, and sweet potatoes into your dog's diet. Lightly steam or bake them for super taste and maximum nutrition. White potatoes and steamed white or brown rice are also nutritious.

Many fruits also provide a healthful addition to our dogs' diets. Fruits such as apples, peaches, pears, bananas, and blueberries are high in many valuable vitamins, minerals, and antioxidants. Offer your dog a slice of banana or apple for a snack instead of a traditional doggy biscuit, or add a scoop of blueberries to some yogurt for an immune-boosting breakfast.

Beware of food toxins

Spoiled or moldy foods that contain mold toxins and other **aflatoxins** (mycotoxins produced by several species of fungi) are very toxic to pets and can cause severe gastrointestinal damage and even liver failure. Aflatoxins are the most potent naturally occurring toxins.

As yummy and nutritious as many fruits are for your dog, there are some that you should never feed him. Certain fruits that most people enjoy without problems can prove toxic—and even deadly—to your dog. So, when you are choosing fruits, skip the following:

- Grapes and raisins
- Strawberries
- Citrus fruits

It's not just certain fruits, though, that can spell trouble if ingested by your canine companion. The following foods should never be allowed to pass your dog's lips:

- Alcohol
- Avocados
- Chocolate
- Coffee, tea, and cola
- Nuts (including peanut butter)
- Mushrooms
- Nutmeg
- Onions (Garlic is fine in moderation, and many pet foods use it.)
- Xylitol (the artificial sweetener)

Some like it raw

A raw canine diet consists of animal meat, organ meats (such as the liver, kidney, and heart), some bone, and small amounts of vegetation given in their raw, uncooked state. A major advantage of raw food is that the nutrients—such as amino acids, vitamins, minerals, prebiotics, probiotics, and enzymes—have not been altered or destroyed by the heat of cooking. Keeping the food in its whole, "pristine" form also makes it much more readily bioavailable, providing our dogs with more easily assimilated nutrition per serving than processed foods.

Raw food may also pose much less risk of allergic reaction than its cooked counterparts. In saliva studies of allergic people, researchers found that there was a five times greater allergic reaction to the exact same food when eaten processed versus in its raw, unaltered form. This makes sense, since cooking food breaks down its cellular integrity and exposes **neo-antigens** (new antigens) that were not there in the original raw form.

If we extrapolate these findings to our canine companions, we can surmise that commercially prepared kibble or canned foods—both of which are cooked at high temperatures—may also be exposing neo-antigens created through the heating process. While still nutritious, these foods could pose a higher risk of dietary intolerance or immune reaction, especially for dogs with already compromised immune systems.

Many people are afraid to feed their dogs a raw diet, which is understandable considering the mixed information available on raw food. Even the majority of traditional veterinarians still warn their clients against feeding raw, citing concerns that their patients will become ill from possible bacteria and parasites in raw meats. This fear, although well-meaning, does not take into account the physiological differences between people and dogs, which make them far less prone to illness resulting from contamination. There are several reasons why dogs tolerate raw meats far better than people do, including:

- Dogs have shorter digestive tracts than humans. This lessens the potential of parasites or bacteria causing problems as food passes through.

- The stomach acid of dogs on raw diets is very low, generally between a pH of 1 and 2. These strong acids, which are necessary to break down the proteins in the raw meats, make it much less likely that bacteria will survive in a healthy dog's gut than in a human's, which operates with a stomach pH of around 5.

- Veterinarians do not take into account that salmonella occurs naturally in the digestive tracts of many dogs, regardless of their diet. Even so, these dogs do not become sick.

In addition, freezing meats for at least three weeks kills most parasites. This is a benefit of feeding a frozen-prepared, raw diet, since these diets are properly frozen to ensure the elimination of parasites. Those buying fresh meat can simply freeze it themselves before feeding it to their dogs.

If you're feeding your dog a raw diet, remember to follow all of the same common-sense precautions you would use when cooking raw meat for yourself or your family. This includes thoroughly washing your hands as well as all surfaces, plates, and utensils that come into contact with the raw meat.

Although raw meats, when properly handled and fed, have numerous health benefits for our canine companions, dogs should never be fed raw fish. Fish from certain areas can contain parasitic cysts or **flukes** (flat worm parasites), particularly around the liver. If a dog ingests fish infested with these parasites, he can become very ill. Home freezers typically do not reach temperatures low enough to kill the parasites in fish. Since the origin of fish is often questionable, it is best to avoid feeding any raw fish to your pet.

The good news is that you don't need a degree in canine nutrition to successfully feed your dog a raw diet. Today there are many reputable commercial producers of prepared raw diets. These come packaged in a variety of forms to suite any preference—from frozen patties to nuggets and chubs—and they already contain the proper balance of meats, vegetables, herbs, vitamins, and minerals. All you have to do is remember to defrost your dog's daily portion in the refrigerator and he will be all set with a nutritionally-balanced, raw meal.

Some reputable producers of raw prepared canine diets include:

- Artisan (Grandma Lucy's)
- Aunt Jeni's
- Bravo

- Darwin's Natural

- Fresh is Best

- Nature's Menu

- Nature's Variety

- Oma's Pride

- Pepperdogz

- Primal

- Raw Advantage

- Stella and Chewy's

- Steve's Real Food

- The Honest Kitchen

- Vital Essentials

If you choose to formulate your dog's raw diet yourself rather than purchasing from a commercial source, you should work with someone who is experienced, such as a canine nutritionist or veterinarian. This will ensure that your dog is consuming the proper balance of nutrients properly tailored for his individual needs.

Another important aspect of feeding raw is to realize that the "normal" values for some of the standard diagnostic lab tests do not apply to animals on a raw diet. Studies by one of the authors (WJD) and Dr. Susan Wynn of the Atlanta, GA area found that dogs fed raw meats (natural carnivores) have higher red blood cell and blood urea nitrogen levels than dogs fed cereal-based food (obligate omnivores). The dogs fed raw meats also showed statistically higher hemoglobin, MCH, MCV, MCHC, total protein, albumin, BUN (blood urea nitrogen)/creatinine ratio, sodium, osmolality, and magnesium. These same dogs displayed lower values for total leukocyte, neutrophil, and lymphocyte counts, as well as phosphorous and glucose.

Many veterinarians, however, do not understand the normal variation of lab tests for dogs on raw diets and misinterpret the findings to mean that the dog is ill. Practitioners have been known to send dog guardians into a panic by warning them that a raw diet is destroying their dog's kidneys, because their BUN is 35 and the normal range ends at 30. The poor person, who doesn't understand that dogs fed raw diets exhibit naturally higher BUN levels, thinks that she is killing her beloved pet! The lesson here is that laboratories have developed their normal ranges based on dogs that are fed cereal grain foods. The normal ranges for many of these tests simply do not apply to healthy dogs fed raw diets, and the interpretation of laboratory results for these dogs should take these differences into account.

Although a raw diet is the most nutritionally bio-available and most natural diet for our canine companions, there are times when raw foods should be avoided. Dogs with bowel problems such as gastroenteritis, which might include bouts of vomiting, diarrhea, constipation, or all of the above, should not be fed a raw diet during flare-ups. When the bowel is not moving at its normal rate, there is increased risk for the bacteria present in raw meat to incubate and multiply in the bowel pockets and then to enter the bile duct and damage the liver. This can be fatal. As long as the food does not contain bones, you can lightly cook it during times of illness (Never cook the bones as they can become brittle and splinter, causing a choking hazard.). Once your dog is better, simply transition back to a raw diet. Alternately, you can keep a premium grain-free kibble or canned food on hand for these times.

If feeding your dog a raw diet is unrealistic for your situation, a home-cooked diet is a healthful alternative. There are several informative books on the market that discuss how to prepare a balanced combination of fresh meat, fish, and vegetables, along with small amounts of eggs, yogurt, and low-fat cottage cheese as a wholesome alternative to commercial pet foods. When cooking for your dog, don't become stressed about making every meal "balanced." After all, we don't try to balance each of our own meals or those of our children. Instead, think about providing a nutritional variety of wholesome foods that, over the course of several days or a week, supply your dog with the balanced nutrition his body requires.

Although you can't prevent your dog from becoming hypothyroid, there are lots of steps you can take to strengthen his immune system. Minimizing toxins and feeding a fresh, wholesome diet will help your dog's body to function at its highest level. And that, ultimately, will enable him to continue living life to its fullest for a long time to come. See Photos 16, 17 and 25 in the insert for some happy raw food fed dogs.

Take home points

- Immune-mediated diseases such as autoimmune thyroiditis weaken our dogs' immune systems, leaving them less able to protect themselves from infection and disease.

- Environmental toxins, chemical flea and tick preventives, overvaccination, prescription and non-prescription medications, and poor or improper nutrition all play a role in overtaxing our dogs' immune systems.

- An overtaxed immune system can lead to the "Humpty Dumpty" effect, where the immune system becomes overloaded and "topples" over, in effect crashing.

- By making some simple changes, we can reduce or eliminate toxic stressors in our dogs' environments, helping to remove some of the burden from their immune systems. This is especially important for dogs with compromised immune systems, such as those with autoimmune thyroiditis.

- Chemical flea and tick preventives should only be used under the guidance of a veterinarian, and products containing organophosphates, pyrethroids, and carbamates should not be given due to their high toxicity.

- Medications should be given only when necessary and used in strict accordance with their prescription in order to maximize their benefits and minimize their potential risks.

- Overvaccination, especially in ill or old pets or those that have shown previous adverse reactions, should be avoided. Titer tests can be given to check for immunity rather than automatically administering yearly boosters.

- A diet rich in fresh, wholesome, nutritionally dense foods is vital to helping your dog's immune system remain healthy and able to resist disease.

- Become a good label reader and reduce or eliminate common food allergens such as wheat, corn, soy, milk, eggs, and beef.

- Add leafy-green and yellow-orange veggies to your dog's diet for their high nutritional content.

- A raw diet comprised of animal meat, organ meats, bone, and a small amount of vegetation is healthy for dogs because the nutrients have not been altered or destroyed by the heat of cooking. Raw foods may also pose much less risk of allergic reaction than cooked foods, which can expose neo-antigens.

- People that do not want to feed their dogs a raw diet can prepare fresh meat, fish, potatoes or rice, and vegetables, along with small amounts of eggs, yogurt, and low-fat cottage cheese as a wholesome alternative to commercial pet foods.

- By reducing or eliminating toxins and feeding a fresh, wholesome diet, you can strengthen your hypothyroid dog's immune system and help him live a happy, healthy, long life.

CHAPTER 6

Diagnostic Testing and Interpretation

This chapter is for those who want to know more about the science behind diagnosing thyroid disorders in dogs. Some of you may find that this information goes beyond what you need in order to proactively care for your hypothyroid dog. However, everyone can benefit from understanding why specific tests are necessary in order to accurately diagnose canine hypothyroidism, and how proper interpretation of those tests is as much an "art" as it is a science.

This chapter is especially useful for veterinarians. Since few veterinary schools have experts teaching the latest findings on diagnosing canine hypothyroidism, and the information contained in the textbooks (at the date of this writing) is woefully outdated, many well-meaning veterinarians are still holding firm to the now obsolete screening guidelines they were trained to apply. A chart summarizing the assessment of canine thyroid function is shown in Figure 4.

This chapter will provide the latest research, debunk some widely held myths, and challenge academics to begin a new era of education—one that teaches future generations of veterinarians the correct tests that need to be performed in order to accurately diagnose this most common endocrine disorder of dogs.

Figure 4. Assessment of Canine Thyroid Function

Laboratory Measurement

A. Total T4 and Free T4

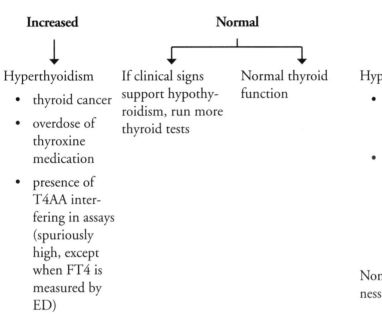

Increased

↓

Hyperthyoidism

- thyroid cancer
- overdose of thyroxine medication
- presence of T4AA interfering in assays (spuriously high, except when FT4 is measured by ED)

Normal

If clinical signs support hypothyroidism, run more thyroid tests

Normal thyroid function

Decreased

↓

Hypothyroidism

- treat and assess clinical and lab response
- if no clinical signs, run more thyroid tests, or repeat tests in 2-4 months

Non-thyroidal illness (NTI)

B. Total T3 and Free T3

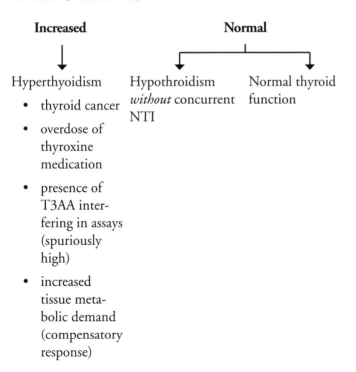

Increased

↓

Hyperthyoidism

- thyroid cancer
- overdose of thyroxine medication
- presence of T3AA interfering in assays (spuriously high)
- increased tissue metabolic demand (compensatory response)

Normal

Hypothroidism *without* concurrent NTI

Normal thyroid function

Decreased

↓

NTI

- identify concurrent illness
- treat and retest in 2-4 months
- presence of T3AA interferring in T3 assay only (spuriously low at MSU Lab only)

85

C. Thyroid Autoantibodies

TgAA

Increased	Normal	Decreased
↓	↓	↓
• Autoimmune thyroiditis • Rabies vaccination within 45 days	• Normal thyroid function • Functional hypothyroidism	N/A

T4AA and/or T3AA

Increased	Normal	Decreased
↓	↓	↓
• Autoimmune thyroiditis	• Normal thyroid function • Functional hypothyroidism	N/A

D. TSH (Thyroid Stimulating Hormone)

Increased	Normal	Decreased
↓	↓	↓
• Primary hypothyroidism • Discordant result (~30% of results)	• Normal thyroid function • Discordant result (~30% of results)	• Secondary or tertiary hypothyroidism (rare) • Secondary to thyroid tumor • Discordant result (~30% of results) • Dog on thyroxine therapy

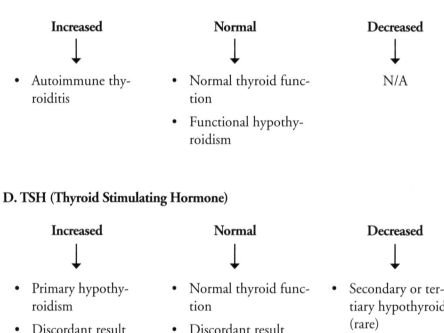

Testing overview for canine thyroid disorder

The following tests all play a role in screening dogs for thyroid disorder:

Total T4. This test measures the total amount of T4 (thyroxine) hormone circulating in the blood—both bound and unbound molecules. More than 99% of T4 hormone is "bound," meaning that it attaches to proteins in the blood and never reaches the tissues. Therefore, a T4 result by itself is often misleading, since it is affected by anything that changes the amount of binding proteins circulating in the blood, (e.g. certain drugs). T4 is still the most popular and widely used initial screening test for thyroid disorder in dogs. As explained below in "The T4 Myth," relying on the accuracy and sensitivity of this test alone is at the heart of the rampant misdiagnosis of canine thyroid disorder. T4 alone is not an accurate indicator of thyroid disorder in dogs, and is often affected by moderate to severe **non-thyroidal illness** (NTI), a disease process other than thyroid disease, and certain medications (e.g. phenobarbital, corticosteroids, and sulfonamides).

Free T4. Serum free T4 represents the tiny fraction (< 0.1%) of thyroxine hormone that is unbound and therefore is biologically active. As the free T4 molecule circulates in the blood and through the pituitary gland's sensor, the level of free T4 tells the pituitary gland whether or not it needs to make more Thyroid Stimulating Hormone (TSH). Although both the bound and free forms of T4 hormone are in circulation, the pituitary gland only recognizes the free molecule. Since protein levels in the blood do not (or only minimally) affect free T4, it is considered a more accurate test of true thyroid activity than the total T4. Free T4 is much less likely to be influenced by NTI or drugs. Both total T4 and free T4 are lowered in cases of hypothyroidism. While endocrinologists may favor the equilibrium dialysis (ED) RIA (radioimmunoassay) method for measuring free T4 because earlier analog methods were less accurate, newer technologies (improved analog RIAs and non-RIA chemiluminescence and other methods) offer alternative and accurate methodology. These new assays do not require radioisotopes and so are environmentally "green" and are also faster and less costly.

Total T3. As with total T4, total T3 represents both the bound and unbound forms of T3 circulating in the blood. Measuring serum T3 alone is not considered an accurate method of diagnosing canine thyroid disorder, as this hormone reflects tissue thyroid activity and is often influenced by concurrent NTI. It is, however, useful as part of a thyroid profile or health screening panel. For example, if levels of total T4, free T4, and total T3 are all low, the patient more likely suffers from an NTI rather than hypothyroidism. If total T3 levels are high or very high in a dog not receiving thyroid supplementation, the patient most likely has a circulating T3 autoantibody (the most common type), which has **spuriously** (falsely) raised the T3 and/or free T3 level.

Free T3. As with free T4, less than 0.1% of T3 molecules circulate freely in the blood and are biologically active. The blood's free T3 level tells the pituitary gland whether or not it needs to produce more TSH. Levels of both total and free T3 may be elevated slightly in **euthyroid** (normal thyroid function) dogs with increased tissue metabolic demands, and are typically spuriously high or very high in dogs with T3 autoantibodies. Both total T3 and free T3 are typically normal in cases of hypothyroidism, unless the disease has been present and undiagnosed for some time, or the dog has concurrent NTI.

Canine Thyroglobulin Autoantibodies (TgAA). Elevated thyroglobulin autoantibodies are present in the serum of dogs with autoimmune thyroiditis, which, of course, is the heritable form of hypothyroidism. As discussed earlier, as much as 90% of cases of canine hypothyroidism result from the heritable condition. TgAA is especially important in screening breeding stock for autoimmune thyroiditis, as dogs testing positive for TgAA should not be bred. The commercial TgAA test can give false negative results if the dog has received thyroid supplement within the previous 90 days, thereby allowing unscrupulous owners to test dogs while on treatment to assert their normalcy, or to obtain certification with health registries such as the OFA Thyroid Registry or Thyroid GOLD™. False negative TgAA results can also occur in about 8% of dogs verified to have high T3 autoantibody and/or T4 autoantibody. The confirmatory version of this test is preferred, as the reagents have been treated to remove any non-specfic binding (NSB) proteins. Furthermore, false positive TgAA results may be obtained if the dog has been vaccinated within the previous 30-45 days for rabies, or very occasionally in cases of NTI. As discussed in Chapter 5, vaccinating dogs with polyvalent vaccines containing rabies virus or rabies vaccine alone has been shown to induce production of antithyroglobulin autoantibodies. This represents an important finding with implications for the subsequent development of hypothyroidism.

T3 Autoantibody (T3AA)/T4 Autoantibody (T4AA). These autoantibodies affect the ability to measure T4 and T3 accurately with most thyroid assay methods. In the presence of high levels of circulating T3AA and/or T4AA, the autoantibody interferes with the ability of the test antibody **reagent** (reacting substance) to detect the hormone being measured. The result is a spuriously *high* reading of T3 (reported as spuriously *low* if measured at Michigan State University's (MSU) Diagnostic Lab) and free T3 or T4 and free T4. However, if the free T4 is measured by the ED technique, the T4AA will be removed by the dialysis step and not be detected. Thus, the presence of T4AA may go unnoticed if free T4 is only measured by the ED method. Fortunately, most circulating antibodies are against T3 (~70%), some affect both T3 and T4 (~25%), and only a few affect T4 alone (~5%).

Most cases of autoimmune thyroiditis exhibit elevated serum TgAA levels, whereas only about 20-40% of cases have elevated circulating T3 and/or T4AA. Thus, the presence of elevated T3 and/or T4AA confirms a diagnosis of autoimmune thyroiditis, but underestimates its prevalence, as negative (non-elevated) autoantibody levels do not rule out thyroiditis.

Endogenous Canine TSH (Thyroid Stimulating Hormone). In primary hypothyroidism, as free T4 levels fall, pituitary output of TSH rises. As discussed in Chapter

Photos 1 and 2: Golden mix suffered from obesity before thyroid therapy (left) and after thyroid therapy (right).

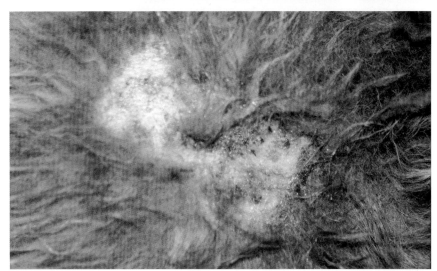

Photo 3: Akita with chronic "hot spots" (pyoderma).

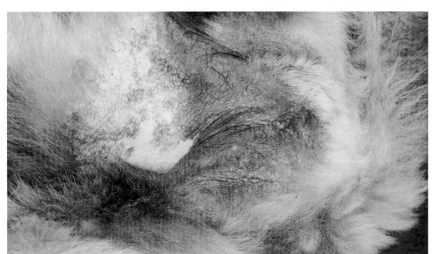

Photo 4: Same Akita with hyperpigmentation.

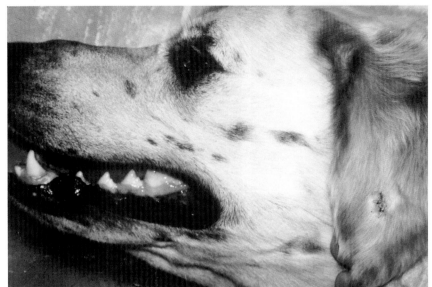

Photo 5: Golden Retriever with facial patchy hair loss.

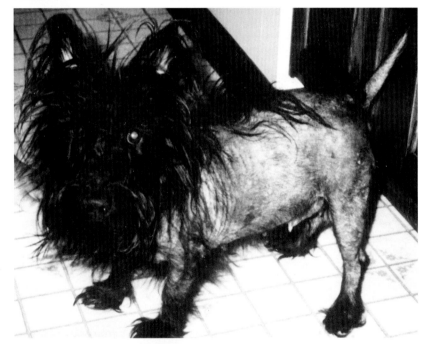

Photo 6: Scottie with marked hair loss.

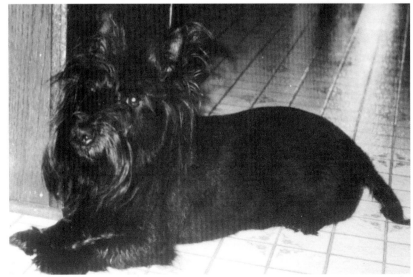

Photo 7: Same Scottie after thyroid therapy.

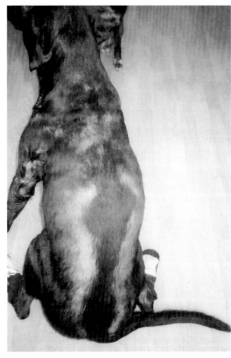

Photos 8 and 9: Pointer mix with sad face, marked hair loss and bilateral striped hair loss.

Photo 10: Josie is a Llewellin Setter (a field strain of English Setter) that was becoming behaviorally abnormal, reclusive and antisocial. We diagnosed thyroiditis and within several weeks on thyroxine therapy, he is back to normal. This is his post-treatment normal look and interaction with others.

Photo 11: Tessie is a young Cocker Spaniel showing the typical crusty skin lesions of hypothyroidism before treatment.

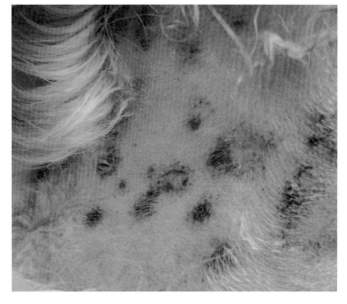

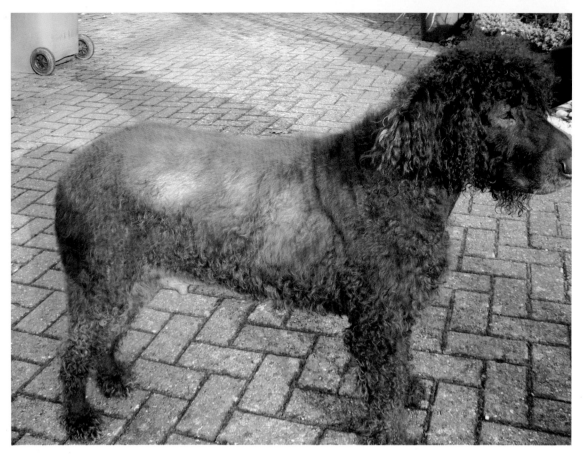

Photo 12: Ruffian, an Irish Water Spaniel with hair loss due to thyroid problems.

Photo 13: Damion is a young adult GSD with horrible dry flakey skin as a result of his hypothyroidism. This is before treatment with thyroxine.

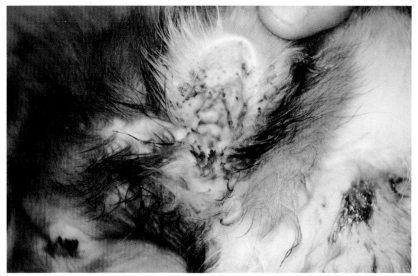

Photo 14: A Sheltie pup suffering from vaccinosis.

Photo 15: The same Sheltie as an adult after no longer receiving vaccines.

Photo 16: (left) Sheltie fed chemically preserved pet food.
Photo 17: (above) Same Sheltie on fresh home-cooked food.

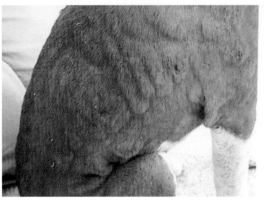

Photo 18: (upper left) Basenji with severe immune-mediated disease (skin ulcerations).

Photo 19: (upper right) Same Basenji with hives.

Photo 20: (lower left) Same Basenji healed.

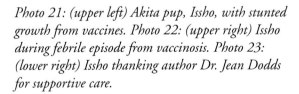

Photo 21: (upper left) Akita pup, Issho, with stunted growth from vaccines. Photo 22: (upper right) Issho during febrile episode from vaccinosis. Photo 23: (lower right) Issho thanking author Dr. Jean Dodds for supportive care.

Photo 24: Kodak, after thyroid therapy.

Photo 25: Shiba Inu with epilepsy eating home-cooked, grain-free diet.

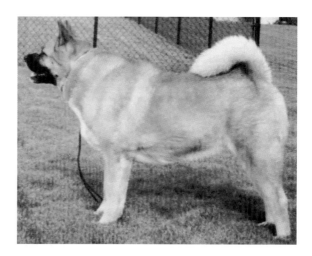

Photos 26: (upper right) Miso before thyroid therapy suffering from obesity.

Photo 27: (left) Miso after thyroid therapy.

Photos 28 and 29: Soshi before (left) and after (right) thyroid therapy.

Photo 31: Molly, a healthy Weimaraner puppy from a family with autoimmune diseases.

Photo 30: Roan, a Drahthaar, ancestor of the German Wirehaired Pointer, a breed prone to thyroiditis today.

1, since about 95% of thyroid hormone regulation in humans is controlled by TSH, it is a highly accurate screening for hypothyroidism. However, only about 70% of thyroid hormone regulation in dogs is controlled by TSH, so this test shows relatively poor predictability. The remaining 30% of a dog's thyroid regulation is controlled by growth hormone, which, like TSH, is manufactured, stored, and secreted by the pituitary gland. For this reason, the TSH test provides a false negative or false positive result in approximately 30% of canine cases. So, although elevated TSH usually indicates primary thyroid disease, there is 20-40% discordance observed between expected and actual results in normal dogs as well as in hypothyroid dogs or those with NTI.

The T4 myth

The vast majority of veterinarians believe that serum T4 alone is adequate as the first screening for a thyroid problem, and that only if T4 is abnormal should further testing be pursued. This misconception, which is still perpetuated today by academics at veterinary schools and consultants for veterinary reference labs throughout the country, is a huge obstacle to accurately diagnosing canine thyroid disorders. Additionally, current veterinary medical textbooks have stated that if a dog has a T4 level above 2 ug/dl (26 nmol/L), there is no need to perform other thyroid testing because the dog has a normal thyroid. This statement is false and misleading, as the T4 result fails to identify any cases of thyroiditis in which elevated thyroid autoantibodies are present!

Many dog guardians are sent away by veterinarians who insist—based solely on a normal or low-normal serum T4—that the dog does *not* suffer from thyroid disease. These poor people inevitably spend many months and can spend thousands of dollars trying to find out what is wrong with their dog until, hopefully, they one day come across someone who conducts a proper thyroid screening profile (see below).

The only way that true progress can be made in the diagnosis of canine thyroid disorder is when veterinarians realize that serum T4 alone is not a reliable method of initial screening, as there are many circumstances in which it can provide misleading results. T4 alone can overdiagnose hypothyroidism in the presence of NTI (such as chronic yeast infections, liver and bowel disorders, and kidney disease—just a few of many examples) or with the use of certain drugs (corticosteroids, phenobarbital, and sulfonamides); it inaccurately assesses the adequacy of thyroxine therapy; and it fails to detect autoimmune thyroiditis.

Furthermore, larger veterinary reference labs are now performing T4 testing on an autoanalyzer along with the serum chemistry profile. These automated analyzer T4 tests frequently read too low in comparison to species-specific RIA or non-RIA T4 assays in healthy dogs. They may also read low in dogs receiving thyroxine supplement or older cats with hyperthyroidism. Thus, the clinician may increase the thyroxine dose of a dog or miss the diagnosis of a hyperthyroid cat based on inaccurate results.

The bottom line: Veterinarians should *not* use T4 as the first screening test for hypothyroidism, and dog guardians should not let their veterinarian convince them to do so. If the T4 is low, you will not know whether the values are accurate without performing additional tests. If it's normal you may miss the diagnosis altogether, because there could be an antibody preventing you from even seeing it. Our dogs certainly deserve a more accurate diagnostic tool for such an important condition!

Case study

Pretty Girl, a seven-year-old, intact female Shetland Sheepdog, exhibited all the classic symptoms of hypothyroidism (slight weight gain, extensive hair loss on the neck and lower torso near her underbelly, skin discoloration and irritation with yeasty odor, thin and rough hair, and a dull coat). Pretty Girl's guardians requested a thyroid profile because their research on her symptoms explained that hypothyroidism was a fairly common problem in Shelties. Also, other breeders told them that Shelties tend to have much higher normal levels of thyroid hormones than many other breeds, so it is often difficult to get a correct diagnosis in this breed. (This is not so, as their thyroid levels are similar to those of other small breed dogs.)

Pretty Girl's regular veterinarian ran a "complete thyroid profile" and told her guardians that it was normal. He then referred them to a dermatologist. However, when they received a copy of the lab results, they discovered that only two tests had actually been performed—a free T4 by equilibrium dialysis (ED) and a TSH. This is a rather typical profile ordered when clinical veterinarians think they need more than a simple T4 test, yet it falls far short of a "complete thyroid profile!"

The free T4ED result was clearly normal, but the TSH was quite high. These results were confusing because a high TSH level is classically seen in most cases of primary hypothyroidism, whereas the mid-range free T4 didn't fit.

So, what was wrong with this diagnosis? It's simple: Shelties frequently have autoimmune thyroiditis with elevated thyroid autoantibodies. However, none of these values were measured.

For example, if Pretty Girl had shown elevated T4 autoantibodies (T4AA), these would have been removed and not detected by the dialysis step in the free T4ED method used. If she had shown elevated T3 autoantibodies (T3AA), these would not have been detected either, as no T3 or free T3 assays were run. Finally, her TgAA also was not measured. Pretty Girl needed more thyroid testing to confirm the clinical impression that she was indeed hypothyroid.

The unfortunate thing about Pretty Girl's situation—and so many other dogs like her—is that veterinarians are not taught correctly about what thyroid tests need to be run. And, if the "professionals" do not know, how on earth would the guardian?

Follow up results: Pretty Girl's serum was sent to one of the author's (WJD) diagnostic lab, Hemolife, a division of Hemopet, a non-profit animal blood bank and greyhound rescue/adoption program. Located in Garden Grove, California, Hemolife provides comprehensive laboratory diagnostic work and interpretation of data to veterinarians worldwide and individual animal owners through their veterinarians. Hemolife provides the most comprehensive diagnostic profiles for detecting and interpreting autoimmune thyroiditis and hypothyroidism, with reference ranges based on age, sex, breed, and activity. The Hemolife laboratory discovered that Pretty Girl's T4AA and T3AA were elevated, and that her TgAA level was also very high. These results confirmed that Pretty Girl indeed had heritable autoimmune thyroiditis that had progressed to hypothyroidism, which had already manifested with her clinical signs.

The author's recommendation was to immediately begin thyroxine therapy twice daily and, after she was clinically improved, to spay her during her next anestrus period in between heats.

After beginning therapy for thyroiditis, Pretty Girl improved dramatically and was spayed. Her guardians were thrilled with her progress and were so happy that they had "their little dog" back.

Case study

Moses, an eight-year-old, neutered male Golden Retriever, weighed 75 pounds and suffered from longstanding weight gain and skin disease. These clinical issues worsened every fall. His veterinarian diagnosed hypothyroidism and placed him on synthetic thyroxine at 0.6 mg twice daily, but it was given with meals. A recheck T4 level was done a month later and was quite low (0.8 µg/dL). The dose of thyroxine was then increased to 0.8 mg twice daily. The recheck T4 a month later was still too low, so the thyroxine dose was increased to a whopping 1.6 mg twice daily (enough for a 250-pound dog)! This time, instead of having the T4 measured by autoanalyzer at the reference lab, the sample was sent to the lab of author, WJD. T4, T3, free T4, free T3, and TgAA were measured. The TgAA was normal, but all four of the other thyroid analytes were extremely high. The thyroxine dose was reduced in stepwise fashion every two weeks until the correct dose for his weight (0.6 mg twice daily) was reached. He is now doing well.

This case illustrates three points: measuring T4 alone can be misleading; measuring T4 on an automated analyzer can read too low; and giving thyroxine with meals will impair its absorption.

What really constitutes a "complete" baseline thyroid profile?

The initial thyroid profile should be comprehensive enough to accurately identify or rule out thyroid disorder, and to determine whether or not the condition is heritable autoimmune thyroiditis. As emphasized above, serum T4 alone is not sufficient for this purpose.

A complete baseline thyroid screening (referred to at the Hemopet lab as the "Thyroid 5" panel) typically includes:

- T4
- T3

- free T4
- free T3
- TgAA

If a dog is brought in for a general wellness exam or with signs of an illness, the Hemopet Thyroid 5 panel (or an equivalent profile conducted at a lab such as MSU or other veterinary school university diagnostic lab, Antech Diagnostics, or Idexx Laboratories) should be combined with a CBC, Super-Chemistry, urinalysis, and a comprehensive physical examination. However, if the dog is simply coming in for genetic screening or a thyroid profile, only the Thyroid 5 or equivalent profile is necessary.

There are several options for follow-up testing, based on the results of the initial Thyroid 5 panel. The goal is always to balance affordability with accuracy.

If the dog's TgAA autoantibodies are negative on the initial screening and he is diagnosed as hypothyroid based on a low T4 and free T4, with normal T3 and free T3, a Thyroid 4 panel (T4, T3, free T4, free T3) is sufficient for retesting (as long as the dog has been placed on thyroid hormone replacement therapy).

If budget is a serious concern for the guardian and the dog is on thyroid replacement therapy, a Thyroid 2 panel (T4 and free T4) could suffice for a routine follow-up. However, the Thyroid 4 is preferable, since we ideally also want to look at T3 and free T3 to assess whether any non-thyroidal issues are present in the dog's body.

In contrast, if the TgAA is elevated on the initial screening, a Thyroid 5 (or its equivalent) *must* be conducted at every recheck to monitor whether the dog's autoantibody level is progressively being lowered based on the therapy. If it isn't, the therapy is not working properly and needs to be re-evaluated, or the dose adjusted.

If the dog's T4, T3, free T4, and free T3 values are normal but his TgAA is high, you still must treat the patient in order to stop the progression of the disease. This is true even if the dog is a prize-winning show dog with no outward signs of a thyroid condition at the time of testing. If his TgAA level is high, he should not be used for breeding and should be placed on hormone replacement therapy immediately. Many people (including veterinarians) believe that it makes clinical sense to wait for the dog to "get sick" before treating him. This "ticking time bomb" approach makes no sense at all. The fact is that the dog *is* sick, and in the vast majority of cases will only become sicker, if left untreated. Only with the proper therapy can he regain his health.

Many veterinarians also see no value in measuring the free, unbound hormones (free T4, free T3) as part of a complete thyroid profile. However, this could not be further from the truth. As discussed above, free T4 and free T3 are the sensing hormones the body uses to determine whether or not it will produce more TSH. It is the circulating levels of free T4 and free T3 that the pituitary gland senses and which determine how much TSH the gland needs to put out in order to stimulate (when thyroid levels are low) or inhibit (when thyroid levels are high) thyroid hormone output from the thyroid gland.

Measuring free T3 in combination with T3 is especially important, as these two hormones, in working together, signal what's happening in the tissues. When the T3 and free T3 are very low together, it tells us that there is a non-thyroidal problem occurring in the body. Alternatively, if the T3 and free T3 are very high and the dog is not taking an overdose of thyroid hormone, it is usually spuriously high, indicating the presence of an antibody against T3 in the blood that's blocking the correct measurement. Those spuriously high levels are a flag for autoimmune thyroiditis. Another reason that T3 and free T3 can be high is from the compensatory effect resulting from an increased metabolic demand from the body's tissue (e.g. obesity, chronic stress, athleticism).

To help control overall costs of testing, the Hemopet lab does not include the T3AA and T4AA tests as part of the baseline Thyroid 5 profile, but instead adds them on later, if appropriate. This is a simple matter of weighing the advantages of including the tests initially with the cost to the client, the additional time it takes, and the additional reagent required. The Thyroid 5 profile identifies about 92% of autoimmune thyroiditis cases based on the elevated TgAA levels. In the remaining 8% of dogs that are TgAA negative but still suffer from thyroiditis, the T4, free T4, and/or T3 and free T3 levels will be high, providing a "red flag" that further testing is required.

Although the Thyroid 5 (or equivalent) panel is extremely accurate, there is still a small percentage of dogs who do not test positive for autoantibodies, but will show lymphocytic thyroiditis if you biopsy their thyroid gland. Routine biopsies simply are not practical, however. This butterfly shaped organ is so tiny that removing even a miniscule portion could induce scarring and prove detrimental to the dog's health. Recent studies suggest that ultrasonography of the neck may reveal an enlarged thyroid gland in cases of thyroiditis.

Analyzing the thyroid panel

Conducting the proper tests, as described above, is half of the thyroid diagnostic puzzle. The other half is understanding how to accurately interpret these tests. Analyzing thyroid panel results is as much an art as it is a science. You cannot judge whether or not a dog's thyroid is functioning optimally based solely on the laboratory's "normal" reference range. Many other factors must also be considered.

Firstly, optimal reference ranges for canine thyroid analytes need to be defined by age, breed, and size. Young animals are growing and need more thyroid activity, whereas geriatrics require less energy. Further, the metabolism of large breeds is different from that of small breeds, and Sighthounds differ metabolically from all other breed types. Other issues, such as lifestyle, weight, and sex should also be considered. No two dogs are alike. Each animal's individual situation must be taken into account and balanced against the laboratory's normal reference range in order to determine an accurate diagnosis.

In addition, every lab has a slightly different range, so what's normal for one could be abnormal for another. If a dog's blood sample is sent to "Lab A" for one screening and "Lab B" for a follow-up, these numbers could vary significantly. Many people memorize a "normal" number and compare that number for the same dog taken from different labs, not realizing that there can be a variation from lab to lab. Lab reference ranges can change as reagents or assay methods change, so check the lab print-out each time you wish to assess and compare results.

Below are Hemopet's current reference ranges for the canine population:

Puppy/Adolescent

As anyone who has watched their tiny puppy sprout into a mammoth adult can attest, a pup's body grows at an astounding rate. This rapid level of development requires quite a fast metabolism and, along with it, higher thyroid hormone output. For optimal health, young dogs under 15-18 months of age should have thyroid baseline levels in the upper half of the adult normal ranges. This is because puppies and adolescent dogs require higher levels of thyroid hormones as they are still growing and maturing.

Hemopet's general reference ranges for puppy and adolescent dogs
Current reference ranges from Hemopet/Hemolife using non-RIA methods.

Expected Levels Category	T4 µg/dL	FT4 ng/dL	T3 ng/dL	FT3 pg/mL
Puppy/Adolescent	1.60 - 3.80	0.90 - 2.50	35 - 70	1.6 - 3.5

Adult

Adult dogs require less metabolic energy than puppies. Their bones, tissues, and organs are fully developed, and that frenzied energy of puppy-hood has transitioned into a calmer, "grown up" temperament.

The normal reference ranges for thyroid analyses of healthy adult dogs are similar for most breeds, although differences do exist based on size and breed. Giant breeds have lower basal thyroid levels, while Sighthounds have the lowest of any category (see charts below).

Lifestyle also plays an important role in determining optimum thyroid levels. Many adult canines are working dogs or enjoy participating in agility competitions. These very active animals have higher metabolic testing profiles than a "couch potato." Case in point: In Alaska, during the training season for the Iditarod, the dogs exhibit quite different thyroid values than when they are not training. During the off-season, their metabolic needs lessen with their reduced levels of activity. Even the changing diurnal rhythms and the light/dark cycle fluctuations affect the dogs' metabolic profiles, and their corresponding optimal thyroid output.

It isn't just Alaskan race dogs that illustrate this point, however. Even two dogs of the same size and breed can vary dramatically if one runs several miles each day and the other sleeps in! The lesson is that dogs cannot be "stereotyped" or classified. Just like people, they are individuals and their metabolic needs are in large part determined by their specific circumstance. This is why we say that interpreting thyroid profiles is as much an art as it is a science.

Hemopet's general reference ranges for adult dogs
Current reference ranges from Hemopet/Hemolife using non-RIA methods.

Optimal Levels Category	T4 µg/dL	FT4 ng/dL	T3 ng/dL	FT3 pg/mL
Adult	1.40 - 3.50	0.85 - 2.30	35 - 70	1.6 - 3.5

Geriatric dogs

Just like people, dogs become more sedentary as they age and therefore require less energy. Since older animals beyond eight or nine years of age have slower metabolisms, baseline thyroid levels of euthyroid dogs may be slightly below midrange.

Care must be taken to not administer too much thyroxine per pound of body weight to a senior dog. It might be tempting to want your geriatric dog bouncing off the walls with energy, but this will certainly not bode well for his older heart and other tissues.

Hemopet's reference ranges for geriatric dogs
Current reference ranges from Hemopet/Hemolife using non-RIA methods.

Optimal Levels Category	T4 µg/dL	FT4 ng/dL	T3 ng/dL	FT3 pg/mL
Geriatric	1.20 - 3.00	0.70 - 1.75	30 - 70	1.6 - 3.5

Large breeds

Since large and giant breed dogs have slower metabolisms than smaller breeds, don't expect the optimum basal thyroid levels of a St. Bernard to be the same as a Yorkie. As you'll see in the chart below, the normal reference range for large breed dogs is actually similar to that of geriatric dogs. Optimum thyroid levels of healthy giant breeds fall between the lower end and midpoint of these ranges. This is very important to take into account when administering thyroid medication. After all, just as you don't want your senior dog to act like a puppy, you don't want your Great Dane behaving like a Chihuahua! Also, the young large breed puppy or adolescent should have thyroid levels in the upper half of these ranges, whereas the levels of a geriatric large breed dog should fall in the lower half.

Hemopet's general reference ranges for large breed dogs
Current reference ranges from Hemopet/Hemolife using non-RIA methods.

Optimal levels category	T4 µg/dL	FT4 ng/dL	T3 ng/dL	FT3 pg/mL
Large breed	1.20 - 3.00	0.75 - 1.80	30 - 70	1.6 - 3.5

Sighthounds

Sighthounds have the lowest basal thyroid levels of any canine group. The typical thyroid levels for healthy Sighthounds fall at or just below the established laboratory reference ranges.

Sighthound breeds include:

- Afghan Hound
- Azawakh
- Basenji
- Borzoi
- Chart Polski (Polish Greyhound)
- Greyhound
- Ibizan Hound
- Irish Wolfhound
- Italian Greyhound
- Peruvian Inca Orchid
- Podengo Portugueso (Portuguese Hound; Grande, Medio and Pequeno)
- Silken Windhound
- Pharaoh Hound
- Rhodesian Ridgeback
- Saluki
- Scottish Deerhound
- Sloughi
- Thai Ridgeback
- Whippet

Hemopet's reference ranges for Sighthounds
Current reference ranges from Hemopet/Hemolife using non-RIA methods.

Optimal levels category	T4 µg/dL	FT4 ng/dL	T3 ng/dL	FT3 pg/mL
Sighthound	0.90 - 2.00	0.50 - 1.20	30 - 70	1.6 - 3.5

Remember, none of these reference ranges is cut in stone, and no dog falls into an absolute stereotype. A major mistake made by both veterinarians and unaware dog guardians is to believe that if a dog's numbers fall inside the reference ranges then they are normal and if they fall outside of the reference ranges, they are abnormal. This is likely to be misleading. The ranges are merely a guideline and are not meant to serve as absolute numbers for individual dogs. Each dog's "normal" will depend on a variety of factors, including his age, breed, size, and lifestyle. For example, a puppy or adolescent Sightbound should have thyroid values in the upper half of these ranges, whereas values for a geriatric Sighthound should fall in the lower half.

Genetic screening for thyroid disease

Complete baseline thyroid panels and thyroid antibody tests are effective tools used for genetic screening to evaluate apparently healthy animals for breeding. As discussed above, tests for TgAA and circulating thyroid autoantibodies (T3AA and T4AA) are especially important for this purpose. A bitch with antithyroid antibodies (TAAs) in her blood may pass these along to her puppies in her colostral milk. Also, any dog with elevated TAAs can eventually develop clinical symptoms of thyroid disease or become susceptible to other autoimmune diseases because his immune system is impaired. Therefore, TAA prescreening can prove very important for ruling out heritable autoimmune thyroiditis in potential breeding stock.

Thyroid testing for genetic screening purposes is unlikely to be meaningful before puberty. Screening is initiated, therefore, once healthy dogs and bitches have reached sexual maturity (between 10-14 months in males and during the first anestrous period for females following their maiden heat). Anestrus is a time when the female sexual cycle is quiescent, thereby removing any influence of sex hormones on baseline thyroid function. This period generally begins 12 weeks from the onset of the previous heat and lasts one month or longer. The interpretation of results from baseline thyroid profiles in intact females is more reliable when they are tested in anestrus. Thus, testing for health screening is best performed at 12-16 weeks following the onset of the previous heat. Screening of intact females for other parameters like vWD (von Willebrand disease), hip dysplasia, inherited eye diseases, and wellness or reproductive checkups should also be scheduled when the dog is in anestrus.

Once the initial thyroid profiles are obtained, dogs and bitches should be rechecked on an annual basis to assess their thyroid and overall health. Annual results provide comparisons for early recognition of developing thyroid dysfunction. This permits treatment intervention, where indicated, to avoid the appearance or advancement of clinical signs associated with hypothyroidism.

For optimum thyroid function of breeding stock, levels should be close to the midpoint of the laboratory normal ranges, because lower levels may be indicative of the early stages of thyroiditis among relatives of dog families previously documented to have thyroid disease.

The difficulty in accurately diagnosing early thyroid disease is compounded by the fact that some patients with typical clinical signs of hypothyroidism have blood thyroid levels within the normal range. A significant number of these patients will improve clinically when given thyroid medication. In such cases, blood levels of the hormones can be normal, but tissue levels are inadequate to maintain health, and so the patient shows clinical signs of hypothyroidism. This situation applies in a selenium deficiency, for example, as previously discussed. While dogs in this category should respond well to thyroid medication, only experienced clinicians are likely to recognize the need to place these dogs on a six-to-eight-week clinical trial of thyroid supplementation. This approach is safe and clinically appropriate, but it requires rechecking blood levels of thyroid hormones toward the end of the six-to-eight-week period to assure that the patient is receiving the correct dose of medication.

In order to reduce the incidences of heritable autoimmune thyroiditis being passed to future generations, it's important to remove dogs with circulating TAAs from the breeding pool. Dogs that are symptomatic of low thyroid function without the presence of TAAs can be treated with hormone therapy, but should only be bred if important for the future of the breed or dog family, and only with a mate that has completely normal thyroid levels and does not require therapy.

Before breeding two dogs, it's essential to objectively evaluate the "pros" and "cons" of each animal. This is especially important if one or both has a family history of a genetic disorder that could be passed to the offspring. Begin by listing 10 positive attributes of each of the dogs involved. Then list 10 negative qualities. Include both physical and behavioral characteristics, such as various aspects of their health, temperaments, etc. This list will give you a good idea if the breeding prospects are a good match. You wouldn't, for example, want to breed two animals with a short back together. The key is to balance each dog's positive and negative attributes so that they mesh well with those of the potential mate.

Unfortunately, some unscrupulous breeders would rather "turn the other cheek" when it comes to breeding a TAA-positive dog with no clinical symptoms than to follow reputable breeding practices. There is often much to be gained financially and in prestige among peers from breeding a beautiful show dog. Deceitful breeders can choose to treat TAA-positive dogs until the antibody disappears and pretend that the dog never had a problem. Unfortunately, there is nothing that can be done except to be aware that such people exist and to avoid doing business with them.

If you find yourself with a TAA-positive dog from a breeder, and that breeder tells you that the parents and siblings are all normal, ask them when they were last tested. It simply does not make sense for the parents to be normal, as the autoimmune thyroiditis had to originate with at least one of the parents. If the parents are indeed normal, then either the father isn't really the father or the mother isn't really the mother—and that is a whole other breeding and purebred registration issue!

If you are considering purchasing a purebred dog from a breeder or are a breeder, one way to ensure that he is free of thyroid disease is to insist upon proof of certification from Hemopet/Hemolife's "Thyroid GOLD™ Registration System" or the equivalent OFA (Orthopedic Foundation for Animals, Inc.) Thyroid Registry program. The Thyroid GOLD™ Registration System ensures that the registered dog has received the proper diagnostic laboratory tests and interpretation and has been deemed free of autoimmune thyroiditis at the time of testing. Retesting is required annually.

Understanding thyroxine dosing

The typical thyroxine dosage is 0.1 mg per 12-15 pounds of a dog's *optimum* body weight. Since large and giant breeds have slower metabolisms, their requirements are less (0.1 mg per 15-20 pounds of optimum body weight). Sighthounds are also different metabolically, and require even less thyroxine dosage than the large and giant breeds. For Sighthounds, a dose of 0.1 mg per 20 pounds of optimum body weight should suffice. Bear in mind that these doses are significantly greater—as much as 10 times greater—than human doses.

Many lay people make the mistake of comparing a dog's thyroid hormone dosage to a person's. However, there is no correlation, since our metabolisms are much slower. As discussed in Chapter 1, the half-life of both T3 and T4 hormone is much faster in dogs than in people (every 12-16 hours in a dog versus every five-to-seven days in a person). It's critical to recognize this difference in metabolic functioning in order to understand canine thyroxine dosing. Through the years, dog guardians have called the Hemopet lab astounded by the prescribed hormone dose, unable to understand why it is so much greater than a typical human dose. We have even seen instances where pharmacists take it upon themselves to lower the dose prescribed by the dog's veterinarian (i.e., from 0.5 mg to 0.05 mg), assuming that the veterinarian misplaced the decimal point! In such cases, the poor dogs took the thyroxine for months without any improvement—and the poor guardians were pulling their hair out wondering why the medication wasn't working. Once the decimal point debacles were straightened out and the correct doses administered, the dogs of course improved.

Rest assured that your veterinarian is correct—regardless of what the pharmacist or your *Physician's Desk Reference* indicates. Thyroxine dosing is one area in which our dogs do not mimic furry little people.

Sub-clinical (borderline-low) hypothyroidism

Some dogs with suppressed thyroid functioning still test within the laboratory's "normal" references ranges. These dogs are said to suffer from sub-clinical—or borderline-low—hypothyroidism. Sub-clinical hypothyroidism is a controversial topic within the veterinary community, since dogs with borderline-low hypothyroidism often display none of the typical clinical symptoms of full-blown hypothyroidism (weight gain, skin and coat problems, and lethargy, for example). However, there is substantial empirical evidence that animals with borderline-low hypothyroidism experience increased issues of aberrant behavior, especially aggression, and also commonly suffer from inflammatory bowel disease.

Understanding how to diagnose sub-clinical hypothyroidism is critical, especially when many veterinarians simply dismiss borderline readings as normal because they fall within the laboratory's reference ranges.

A dog is generally considered to suffer from sub-clinical hypothyroidism if his hormone levels fall within the lower 50% of the normal range. To calculate the 50% point, simply add the lower and highest values of the range and divide by two. For example, in an adult dog, the 50% point is calculated as follows:

T4
Normal range = 1.40-3.50 µg/dL
1.40 + 3.50 = 4.9
4.9 / 2 = 2.43
2.43 = 50% of the normal range for adult T4.

Free T4
Normal range = 0.85-2.30 ng/dL
0.85 + 2.30 = 3.15
3.15 / 2 = 1.58
1.58 = 50% of the normal range for adult free T4.

T3
Normal range = 35-70 ng/dL
35 + 70 = 105
105 / 2 = 52.5
52.5 = 50% of the normal range for adult T3.

Free T3
Normal range = 1.6-3.5 pg/mL
1.6 + 3.5 = 5.1
5.1 / 2 = 2.55
2.55 = 50% of the normal range for adult free T3.

If your dog's thyroid levels fall in the lower 50% of the reference range and he exhibits aberrant behavior or other signs related to hypothyroidism, he may benefit from hormone supplementation. Talk to your veterinarian about a low-level trial dose of thyroxine. If you notice positive changes in your dog's behavior or other clinical issues once he's on the medication and follow-up testing shows an improvement in his thyroid levels, it's certainly worth continuing to administer the medication for the long-term.

Case study

Miso, a four-year-old, intact female red Akita, was a show champion and working agility dog who kept gaining weight even though her experienced guardian didn't overfeed her, and her skin and coat quality were excellent. She gradually got so heavy that her shoulders were bearing too much weight to allow her to safely clear the agility course jumps. Her frantic guardian requested a thyroid profile because she was convinced that Miso must have hypothyroidism as the underlying reason for the weight gain.

Miso's veterinarian ran a "complete thyroid profile" and told her guardian that it was low-normal, but not really low enough to account for the weight issue. In discussing the results, the client asked the veterinarian if he would contact one of the authors (WJD) to obtain her opinion. After reviewing the situation and the sub-optimal thyroid profile results, it was mutually decided to put Miso on a moderate dose of thyroxine supplement given twice daily for six weeks. But, in those days, prior to the 2000s, we were unaware of the importance of giving the thyroid medication apart from meals, in order for it to be fully absorbed. This was further complicated because Miso ate a premium performance diet, which contained plenty of calcium to interfere with absorption of the thyroxine.

As expected, the trial course of thyroxine did little to help Miso lose weight. Her veterinarian elected to increase the thyroxine dose by 25%, and lo-and-behold, Miso started to lose weight. After four months of thyroid supplementation she had lost 15 of her 20 excess pounds, and was looking svelte and muscled once again. The rest of the story is unremarkable, as Miso returned to top form in agility trials and lived to be 12 years of age, still taking the required dose of thyroxine for her age and weight at the time—given, of course, apart from her meals. See Photos 26 and 27 in the insert.

Again, this case study emphasizes that the laboratory reference ranges are merely guidelines for diagnosing hypothyroidism. They are not cut in stone. As we emphasize throughout this book, when it comes to your dog's thyroid health (and his health in general), trust your instincts. If you notice that your normally happy and easygoing dog suddenly shows signs of aberrant behavior—or if he exhibits other symptoms that could relate to a thyroid disorder—and his levels fall under the 50% mark of the reference range, speak to your veterinarian about a trial of thyroid supplementation.

Take home points

- Outdated or incomplete information taught in veterinary schools perpetuates inaccurate screening for canine thyroid disorder, since many veterinarians are still applying outdated diagnostic methods.

- Tests used to determine thyroid disease include T4, free T4, T3, free T3, TgAA, T4AA, T3AA, and TSH. Their usages and importance depend on the situation of the dog being tested.

- T4 alone is *not* a reliable method of screening for canine thyroid disorder.

- T4 measured by automated autoanalyzer technology can read too low and over-diagnose hypothyroidism, underdiagnose hyperthyroidism, and result in inappropriate use of thyroxine therapy or thyroxine overdosage.

- T4 alone can overdiagnose hypothyroidism in the presence of non-thyroidal illness or with the use of certain drugs, it inaccurately assesses the adequacy of thyroxine therapy, and it fails to detect autoimmune thyroiditis.

- A complete initial thyroid profile should include T4, T3, free T4, free T3, and TgAA.

- Patients with elevated TgAA who do not exhibit clinical signs of hypothyroidism should still be treated to prevent progression of the disease.

- TgAA is the marker for autoimmune thyroiditis, the genetic form of hypothyroidism.

- TgAA prescreening as a minimum should be conducted on all dogs used for breeding to prevent passing along thyroid disorder to the offspring.

- TgAA picks up autoimmune thyroiditis in about 92% of cases. In the remaining 8% percent, the T4, free T4 and/or T3 and free T3 markers will be high (T3 will be low at MSU's Diagnostic Lab), indicating further testing of T4AA and/or T3AA is necessary.

- Understanding how to properly interpret thyroid tests is critical to accurately diagnosing thyroid disorder.

- All dogs are individuals. Factors such as age, breed, size, and lifestyle all play a part in determining a dog's optimal thyroid levels.

- Thyroxine dosing in dogs cannot be compared to humans. Canine dosing is as much as 10 times that of human dosing.

- Just because your dog falls within the laboratory's normal reference ranges does not mean his thyroid is functioning optimally.

- Sub-clinical hypothyroidism occurs when a dog's thyroid gland is functioning sub-optimally, but he still tests within the laboratory's normal reference range.

- Dogs that fall within the lower 50% of the reference range and exhibit clinical symptoms of hypothyroidism may benefit from hormone replacement therapy.

CHAPTER 7

How to Effectively Manage your Dog's Thyroid Disorder

We have discussed a lot of information about canine thyroid disease, from the importance of the thyroid gland and the many conditions related to thyroid disorders to how to assess whether your dog has hypothyroidism. Now, we are going to "bring it all home" and tell you how to apply this knowledge to *your* situation so that you can help *your* dog if you do feel he has a thyroid disorder. After all, that is what really matters!

This is also the chapter where we bring you some wonderful news. If your dog has thyroid disease, you *can* make a huge difference in his diagnosis, treatment, and follow-up care. With your proactive participation, your canine companion will be well on the path to spending many healthy, vibrant years by your side.

The foundation of your dog's thyroid disorder treatment is hormone replacement therapy. Unless your dog receives the proper hormone medication administered correctly and in the accurate dosage, he will continue to suffer unnecessarily from his thyroid disorder.

You will play a critical role in overseeing and managing your dog's hormone replacement treatment. The more you understand about the therapy—including how to administer the proper dosing—the better you can assist your canine companion on his journey to wellness.

Understanding hormone replacement therapy

The majority of dogs (95%-98%) diagnosed with hypothyroidism are treated with thyroxine therapy. As discussed earlier, thyroxine (abbreviated T4, because it contains four iodine molecules) is the hormone produced by the thyroid gland. It is converted primarily in the liver by an enzyme that removes one of the iodine molecules, thereby forming the T3 hormone, which enters the cells. Its function is to regulate the body's metabolism.

When your dog begins thyroxine therapy, your veterinarian will weigh several factors to determine the initial dosing. The most important factors are:

- Age
- Weight
- Breed
- Lifestyle

Let's look at the role each of these variables plays in determining your dog's medicinal dosing.

Age

As we've previously discussed in detail, the thyroid controls the body's metabolic functions. However, as a dog ages, his metabolic needs change. Younger dogs expend a greater amount of metabolic energy to sustain their developing organs and tissues, as well as to fuel their active adolescent lifestyles and perhaps even support pregnancy and lactation. On the other hand, senior dogs require much less metabolic energy as they transition into a more sedentary stage of life. Thyroxine dosing must be adjusted to account for the changing energy requirements that occur due to age. Therefore, a hypothyroid adolescent dog should receive a higher dose of hormone replacement medication per pound of body weight than a senior dog with the same level of hypothyroidism.

In addition, older dogs often have other health considerations that dictate a slow and watchful approach to ensure that they do not receive too much hormone too quickly. If a dog suffers from heart disease, for example, you do not want to start him off right away with the maximum dose of thyroid medication, as you will risk accelerating his heart too quickly. Revving from zero to 160 might be desirable for a sports car, but not for a dog! It is much more desirable to take it slowly and, if need be, to increase the dose after the first retest.

Weight

The typical thyroxine dosage is 0.1 mg per 12-15 lbs of body weight (although this varies by breed), administered orally twice per day. The key to remember is that dosing should be based on a dog's *optimum* weight, not his actual weight. If your dog weighs 65 pounds but his optimum weight is 60 pounds, the correct dose of thyroxine would be 0.5 mg given every 12 hours. If your dog is overweight, don't despair. Since thyroid replacement therapy will increase his metabolic turnover, it will also aid him in fighting the battle of the bulge (providing, of course, that you make the proper lifestyle and nutritional adjustments as well).

Breed

A dog's breed is an important factor in determining proper thyroid replacement dosing. Since smaller breeds have faster metabolisms than large breeds, they require more energy per pound. You might think about this in terms of your dog's diet. Although smaller breeds consume fewer total calories than large breeds, they consume *more calories per pound.* The same is true when it comes to thyroid replacement treatment. Larger breeds have slower metabolisms and are less active, so they do not require as much thyroid hormone per pound of body weight as small breed dogs. For example, if you have a Toy Poodle and a St. Bernard—both of the same age and both with the same level of hypothyroidism—the Toy Poodle will receive hormone replacement medication at the dose of 0.1 mg of thyroxine per 12 pounds of optimum body weight, whereas the St. Bernard will receive 0.1 mg per every 20 pounds of his optimum body weight. Further, as stated earlier, Sighthounds generally need less thyroxine to meet their metabolic demands than other breed types (i.e., only 0.1 mg of thyroxine per every 20 pounds of optimum weight, given twice per day). Remember, for all dogs, that dosage is based on a dog's optimum weight, not his actual weight, and is given at that dose twice per day.

Lifestyle

How would you describe your family situation? Do you and your dog reside together in a tranquil environment, or is he part of a hectic family? Your dog's lifestyle will play a significant role in determining his hormone replacement needs. If you have young children that expect their pet to play with them throughout the day, you want to make sure his daily dose of hormone replacement gives him the energy to keep up with them. On the other hand, if you and your dog live a sedate, quiet life together, you don't want him bouncing off the walls!

Your dog's lifestyle will also help determine how his medicinal dosage is split up between morning and evening. Dogs who use up more metabolic energy during the day—such as pets in active households, competitive athletes, show dogs, or working dogs—may benefit from a slightly higher dose of hormone in the morning and a slightly lower dose at night. These dogs require more metabolic energy during the day and less at night when they are tired, so it makes sense to adjust their dosing accordingly.

Be sure to communicate your dog's daily "lifestyle energy needs" to your veterinarian so the two of you can discuss any necessary adjustments to his dosing.

Monitoring your dog's medicinal dosage

Regular follow-up blood tests are vital to ensure your dog receives the accurate amount of hormone replacement therapy. These blood tests should be performed every six-to-eight weeks until the proper dose is established, then a minimum of once per year thereafter. This is especially important as your dog transitions into his senior years. As we discussed, his metabolism will slow as he ages and his medication will likely need to be re-dosed accordingly.

Don't just think about the dosing of your dog's thyroid medication when it's time for his blood test. Make it a practice to monitor him on a daily basis, watching for any physical or behavioral changes that could indicate a dosing issue. Be sure to include your observations in your canine health journal.

When taken as directed, thyroxine is extremely safe. However, it is important to make sure your dog is receiving the proper dosage based on the variables discussed above, since excessive thyroxine intake can lead to **thyrotoxicosis** (thyroxine overdose), a condition that requires prompt attention by your veterinarian. If you think your dog might have thyrotoxicosis, don't panic. Since the half-life of thyroxine (the time it takes for it to reduce to half its strength in the blood's plasma) is short (12-16 hours) lowering or stopping the dose will quickly revert your dog's metabolism back to normal.

Signs of thyrotoxicosis include:

- Pacing
- Restlessness
- Panting
- Excessive thirst

As discussed below, it's important to remember that thyroxine should be given apart from meals, as it binds to calcium and soy. Give it at least an hour before, or three hours after, each meal to ensure proper absorption.

Just as receiving too much thyroxine is undesirable, so is receiving too little. If your dog is not getting enough hormone therapy to meet his metabolic needs, his health will not improve. If you feel your dog's dosing is inadequate, be sure to have him re-checked and his medicine adjusted accordingly.

Signs of thyroxine underdosing include:

- Itching/scratching
- Lethargy
- Excessive shedding
- Weight gain
- Behavioral issues

You have several advantages over your veterinarian when it comes to monitoring your dog's thyroid medication. You are with him everyday, are intimately familiar with your dog's "normal" physical and behavioral traits, and have a special bond with your pet that enables you to instinctively sense when something "is not right."

You, as the guardian and spokesperson, must become the champion of your dog's well-being. This means "going with your gut," even when it does not agree with your veterinarian. If your dog is on thyroid therapy and is still not acting right, go back to your veterinarian and insist that he be retested. Follow your instincts. Don't ever let anyone intimidate you into thinking you are being silly or overly cautious. If your veterinarian isn't interested in your concerns, find one who is.

Write down daily observations about your dog's physical and behavioral responses to his thyroid medication in your canine health journal. Is his energy level stable throughout the day, or does he experience peaks and valleys? Does he appear jittery or nervous at night? Is he exhibiting any strange behavior, such as uncharacteristic aggression? Keeping a journal to which you can refer during appointments will help you organize your thoughts and maximize your time with your veterinarian. It will also ensure that you don't leave the office kicking yourself because you forgot to mention something important.

When you bring your dog for his periodic rechecks, be certain that the blood sample is drawn four-to-six hours after his morning pill. If taken any sooner or later, you risk an inaccurate reading due to what erroneously appears to be overdosing or underdosing.

Most veterinarians merely test T4 levels during rechecks, however this is insufficient and can even be misleading. See Chapter 6 for options regarding follow-up testing in various circumstances.

Case study

Presto is a 10-year-old, neutered male Greyhound who was diagnosed in 2006 as being hypothyroid based on a very low T4 level (0.3 µg/dL). As this was so much lower than the reference lab's normal ranges for dogs (1.0-4.0 µg/dL), his veterinarian placed him on 1.6 mg of thyroxine once daily, even though Presto had no obvious clinical signs of hypothyroidism, except for intermittent gastrointestinal upsets.

After several weeks, Presto started to shed his coat, which resulted in patchy baldness. He also experienced a dramatic weight loss, from 74 pounds to 68 pounds. Presto also developed a ravenous appetite, seemed "wired" with energy, and had large, foul smelling, and frequent stools. He also began to eat sticks and the bark off trees, and licked the wood floors. His veterinarian decided that Presto's thyroid dose was too high and lowered it to 1.2 mg once daily. Presto did not improve, and he continued to lose weight.

At this point, his owner contacted one of the authors (WJD) for advice and had several questions. Should she be worried about his hair loss? Why were his stools like this? Could it be because thyroid disease affected his ability to absorb nutrients? Should she be adding digestive enzymes and probiotics to his diet? Why was he losing weight and yet full of energy? Since his blood recheck T4 level was only 1.5 µg/dL, did that mean that his dose of thyroxine needed to be increased?

WJD's response: Yikes! Presto's odd behavior and other signs were due to the fact that he was receiving *too much thyroxine* for the slower metabolic rate typical of Sighthounds.

The normal basal thyroid levels of all Sighthounds (see list in Chapter 6) is at the lower end to just below the normal basal reference range for other breed types. Therefore, the dose of thyroxine required by Sighthounds is about half that given to other breed types (i.e., 0.1 mg per 20 pounds of optimum weight, administered twice daily).

As you can see from this information, Presto should have been taking no more than 0.4 mg of thyroxine given twice daily, for a total of 0.8 mg a day. Also, the dose should have been divided equally into two portions rather than being given all at once. Giving thyroxine just once daily, especially to an older dog like Presto, creates a "peak and valley" effect. This is because, as we've discussed earlier, thyroxine has a half-life of only 12-16 hours in dogs, unlike in people, where it has a much slower turnover time of five-to-seven days. This peak and valley has undesirable effects on the cardiovascular system. This is why it is important to achieve a steady state of thyroxine activity by dividing the total daily dose in half and administering it twice daily.

Administering hormone replacement therapy

How and when you administer your pet's thyroid medication will have a tremendous impact on the success of the treatment.

Unfortunately, most veterinarians are as perplexed as their clients when it comes to the issue of whether you should give thyroid medication with food. They simply were not taught this in veterinary school. However, make no bones about it (no pun intended!)—thyroid medication should *not* be given with food. To make matters even more confusing, the product label often states to give it with meals!

Because thyroxine binds to calcium and soy in foods, it must be administered at least one hour before your pet's meal or at least three hours after his meal. If thyroxine is taken with food, it may be absorbed incompletely or too slowly, resulting in low readings on the laboratory blood tests. Your veterinarian will inevitably increase your dog's dose as a result of the misleading readings, only to have the retests continue to read low due to poor absorption. Many frustrated people give up on their dog's thyroid replacement therapy because they think it is not working, when in fact it is merely not being absorbed properly because their veterinarian never told them that it must be given on an empty stomach. The solution was right under their nose the whole time (literally, in their dog's dish). Just stop giving the medication with their food!

If you must "coax" your dog to swallow the pill by placing it inside a small piece of food, choose something that will not interfere, such as a small marshmallow, a bit of creamy peanut butter (but be aware that some dogs react adversely to peanuts), or a cooked green bean. Never wrap the pill in cheese or meat.

Another controversy lies in how often to administer a dog's thyroid medication. Consider this an end to that controversy. Thyroxine must be given twice per day—once in the morning and once in the evening, ideally spaced 12 hours apart.

This makes perfect sense if you think about it. Dividing the medication into two daily portions ensures that your dog will receive a steady state of hormone throughout the day, rather than experiencing a "peak" and "valley" effect that would result from giving only one dose in the morning. Dosing only once per day would result in the dog's heart being revved up for half the day and down for the other half. As we previously discussed, this is obviously undesirable, especially for older dogs.

As mentioned in the "Lifestyle" section earlier in this chapter, there are instances when you might want the morning dose to be greater than the evening dose, such as with working or competition dogs, which exert most of their energy during the day and are tired in the evenings. If you think this makes sense for your dog, be sure to discuss it with your veterinarian. Even if you go this route, you will still need to dose twice per day.

Although most thyroxine medication comes in pill form, there is a liquid available on the market that claims it requires just one dose per day. Even this medication is best given twice daily, regardless of the label's instructions. If your dog is taking liquid thyroxine, be sure to discuss the dosing with your veterinarian.

Another common—and dangerous—mistake people make when it comes to administering their dog's thyroid replacement therapy is to stop the medication because they think their dog is "cured." Dogs with true hypothyroidism are *never* cured: They only *appear* to be cured because they are on the treatment. Stop the treatment, and their symptoms will quickly resurface. Thyroid replacement therapy *manages* a dog's condition; it does not cure it. Once the proper dosing is established, maintenance is as simple as giving your pet his twice-daily pill and periodically checking his blood. But he must always remain on his medication.

Alternatives to thyroxine: natural therapies and supplements

Thyroxine is extremely safe when taken as directed. However, we recognize that some people do not like using any "synthetic" drugs, preferring instead to use "natural" products whenever possible. If you are one of those people, you can substitute natural thyroid extracts made from bovine or porcine thyroid glands for the synthetic thyroxine hormone replacement. Armour Thyroid™, ERFA™ (in Canada), Westhroid™, and Naturethroid™ are all good choices. However, these products contain both T4 and T3 thyroid hormones, so the dosage should be adjusted with that in mind. Also, since dosages of natural thyroid extracts are measured in grains (60 mg = 1 grain), adjusting this to match the equivalent synthetic thyroxine dosage can prove challenging (see Appendix B for a chart on converting natural thyroid extract dosing in grains to their equivalent T4 mcg/mg doses). Bear in mind that these dessicated thyroid extracts will also cost much more, as relatively large amounts must be given to equate to the higher therapeutic needs of dogs.

As an adjunct to your synthetic or natural thyroid replacement therapy, you might also want to use supplements that help support the functions of the thyroid gland.

The most commonly used are products made by Standard Process™, including Thytrophin PMG™ and Thyroid Support™. Although these products usually cannot replace the need for thyroid hormone replacement in true cases of canine hypothyroidism, they have been used successfully to lower the dose of thyroxine or natural thyroid extract needed.

Take home points

- By taking a proactive approach to your dog's thyroid care and management, you *can* make a huge difference in his health.

- Hormone replacement therapy with the thyroid hormone thyroxine is the cornerstone of successfully treating your dog's hypothyroidism.

- Your dog's age, weight, breed, and lifestyle will all affect his medicinal dosing.

- Regular blood tests are needed to ensure your dog is receiving the proper hormone dosage. Test every four-to-six weeks until proper dosing is achieved, then once per year thereafter.

- Monitor your dog's physical and behavioral changes on a daily basis. If anything seems "not right" to you, bring him to your veterinarian for retesting.

- Be sure that your dog's hormone medication is divided into two daily doses.

- Never give your pet's thyroid medication with food.

- Never stop your dog's hormone medication. Hormone replacement therapy *manages* thyroid disease; it does not cure it.

- For those who prefer natural products to synthetics, thyroid extracts made from bovine or porcine thyroid glands are viable substitutes for thyroxine, provided that the equivalent dosing is maintained.

CHAPTER 8

Proactive Care for a Healthy Canine

Congratulations! You are approaching the finish line of a book that will empower you with the knowledge to take control of your dog's health and position yourself as an advocate on his behalf. This chapter will further emphasize what we have been stating all along—that you and you alone must speak up and speak out for your canine companion. All of the knowledge in the world will not help your furry friend, if you do not trust your instincts. By now, we hope that you have the confidence to "stand up" for your dog and realize that you do have the power to make an important (and perhaps even life-saving) difference in his long-term health. Don't ever let yourself be intimidated by professionals who insist that they have all the answers—and that if they *don't* have the answers, then the answers must not exist!

Hopefully, the case studies throughout this book have highlighted how important it is for you, as your dog's trusted guardian, to persevere—even in the face of adversity—until you find the answers. Remember, the answers *are* there. They are sometimes just hiding in the shadows of phantom symptoms and frustrating misdiagnoses.

To that end, let's discuss some proactive steps you can take in playing "doggy detective" for your pet's health—and how to avoid the landmines of misinformation that threaten to lead even the most well-meaning dog parent astray.

Gather information wisely

It may begin with just an inkling that something is "not right." Perhaps your normally playful canine has recently been moping around the house. Or, maybe he suddenly refuses to touch his food. Or, he's had a couple of uncharacteristic "accidents" in the house. Naturally, you are concerned and you want to learn more. And, with all of the information available at, literally, your fingertips, it makes perfect sense to gather as much information as possible to take with you to your veterinarian.

The key is to know how to seek out the most *accurate* information. Be discriminating in what you choose to read—and believe. This starts with selecting the most up-to-date information possible. You wouldn't want to fix your computer with a manual written 10 years ago, would you? Of course not! Technology is advancing so quickly that it's likely a manual written even a couple of years ago would be out of date. The same is true when researching medical topics. New scientific research often means that anything written more than a year or so ago should be considered "old news."

Avoid online landmines

The Internet is a wonderful reference resource because it enables everyone to have access to volumes of information on every conceivable subject—some of it written by top professionals in their fields. On the other hand, the Internet also contains a lot of out-of-date and inaccurate information, and you don't want to rely on that. The two main things to focus on when searching for information online are the credibility of the author and the most up-to-date research.

Since nothing ever really "disappears" once it is posted on the Web, there is the danger of finding articles that were written years ago. These articles may have been relevant—and quite accurate—at the time (and might even have been written by experts), but because they are old, the information contained within them may now be obsolete. Be sure to note the date of the articles you find, and move on or consider this dating if they are old.

On the other hand, there are plenty of current articles that are riddled with misinformation. These articles are often written by "enthusiasts"—people with a strong opinion about a particular subject who are not experts in their field and who do not quote experts. Although the authors are well intentioned, they often rely on nothing more than their own personal experience. Please stay away from these types of articles.

When searching online, start by plugging in the main theme in your search engine. You can be pretty specific in your word choices. Chances are your search will return a large volume of results. Carefully sift through them, cherry-picking the most current articles written by recognized names in their particular field (or articles that interview these experts).

Take friends' advice with a "grain of salt"

Doesn't it seem like our friends become instant experts with all the answers when we have a question about a relationship issue, a medical problem, or a business venture? The problem is that these "instant experts" may have acquired their knowledge by reading the very articles online that we've just advised you to avoid!

We are not saying to completely dismiss friends' advice. After all, one of them might turn out to possess a jewel of information that will enable you to bypass months of frustration and expense and cut right to the answer you are looking for. Or, they could lead you down a wrong path as fraught with obstacles as Dorothy's trek to Oz. The point is that when the woman you bump into every Sunday at the dog park insists that Princess's rash indicates a rare reaction to "fungal spores from Brazil" because she just read something about it online, listen with a somewhat jaded ear. Then, decide whether the "expert lead" is worth pursuing or not.

One of the authors (DL) has a story that perfectly illustrates how friends and acquaintances can wreak havoc on a dog parent's nerves with their well-meaning—but completely erroneous—diagnoses. I was out to dinner with a colleague and his wife one night when I excitedly extracted a photo from my purse of my newly adopted Shepherd mix, Chase. In fact, Chase was such a new addition to my life that this was about the only photo I had of him (this was before snapping pictures on our cell phones was par for the course).

I passed the photo to my colleague's wife with a gleam of pride in my eyes. But, as she glanced down at my beautiful boy, her jaw dropped and her face turned a ghastly shade of white, as if she had just seen a ghost. I asked her what was wrong, to which she bluntly replied, "I think your dog has retinal cancer."

"Check, please!" my colleague shouted, knowing how Chase was already the love of my life and how upset I must certainly be by his wife's proclamation of doom. When I asked the woman to elaborate on her reasons for believing that my dog had retinal cancer, she explained that she had just read an article in a magazine about a child with retinal cancer. Apparently, the child's cancer had been diagnosed because, in a photo, his eyes had cast off an eerie white glow—just as Chase's did in the photo I handed her (I called it his "alien" look)!

Needless to say, I went home that evening quite distressed. The next morning, I contacted a board certified veterinary ophthalmologist in my area and explained the situation. The veterinarian said she had never heard of such a thing in dogs, but to bring Chase in for an exam just to be safe. I did, and thankfully my precious dog's eyes were in perfect health, just as they continue to be upon this writing more than nine years later.

My colleague's wife meant well, of course, but blurting out, "I think your dog has retinal cancer" based on an article in a magazine certainly did not show the best judgment!

Be a detective

In Chapter 5, we talked about many factors that can cause a dog to become sick, from environmental toxins such as pesticides, household cleaners, and mold, to chemical flea and tick preventives, to pharmaceuticals, vaccines, and even improper nutrition. If you notice a change in your dog's health, don't dismiss the possibility that it could have something to do with his surroundings. Put on your thinking cap and engage in a little doggy detective work.

Think carefully about all the things that have changed in your dog's life, even if they seem insignificant to you. Perform a mental checklist that includes the following questions:

- Did you recently remodel or repaint? Perhaps your dog is reacting to chemicals in the paint, or to dust or mold that has been released into the air via the remodeling process.

- Did you spray the lawn with pesticides or treat it with fertilizer? Even if the bag says it's perfectly safe, that doesn't mean your dog won't react to it.

- Did you recently change laundry detergents, floor soaps, rug shampoos, or other household cleaners?

- Did you redo your wood floors, or change from tile to carpet?

- Was your dog recently vaccinated?

- Has he started on any new medications?

- Have you made any changes to his diet or supplements?

- Has someone in your home recently begun taking medication who could have accidentally dropped a pill?

Review the potential toxins listed in Chapter 5 to jog your memory, then think about anything and everything you have recently done differently in or around your home. Don't dismiss anything. Even if it seems like it shouldn't have mattered, maybe it did.

Case study

Bear, an eight-year-old Golden Retriever with chronic inhalant allergies, was presented to one of the authors (WJD) with sores that resembled tiny rupturing blood blisters or boils on his face, underneath his eye, and down to his lips. The interesting thing was that *the sores appeared only on the left side of his face.* When asked what Bear had been doing differently, his guardian realized that although Bear normally slept outside on the porch or on the tile, lately he had been snoozing inside on the rug. And, Bear preferred to lie on his left side! We cultured the sores and discovered Staphylococcus intermedius. Within 24 hours on cephalexin, the sores began to dry up.

The larger issue that remained, however, was to prevent Bear from suffering any further outbreaks. This required eliminating contact between his face and the rug. I advised his guardian to take a clean, pale-colored cotton sheet (white, beige, or cream) and rinse out the sizing in clear water (without using soap). This sheet would then be placed as a "barrier" between Bear and the rug. His guardian was careful to heed my advice and always kept this protective barrier between Bear and the offending surface. His weeping sores have not returned since.

"Shop" for the right health care partner

You wouldn't just walk into a medical doctor's office and proclaim, "I'm here as a new patient" without first knowing a great deal about her. The same holds true when choosing a "primary care" veterinarian for your dog. This relationship will prove crucial to your canine companion's ongoing well-being, so you'll want to make sure that you feel confident about your veterinarian's credentials, experience, and expertise—as well as feeling comfortable that you can enter into an open, mutually-respectful dialog with her about any issue related to your dog's health.

If you are new to an area, have a new dog, or are dissatisfied with the relationship with your current veterinarian, actively seek out a provider with whom you feel you can establish a long-term partnership.

As we mentioned earlier, if utilized correctly, the Internet can provide a wealth of beneficial information. This is also true when researching veterinarians. Many veterinarians now offer extensive Web sites about their practice, so this is the perfect place to begin the screening process. If you've got a few names in mind, begin by visiting their Web sites. Read up on their philosophy and practice areas, view their staff credentials, and explore pictures of their facility. Some veterinarians even offer "virtual tours" of their offices on their sites. From here, you can pick one or two that you would like to interview in person.

You can find a list of holistic veterinarians in your area from the American Holistic Veterinary Medical Association (http://www.ahvma.org). This site provides a detailed section to help you "Find a Holistic Veterinarian" where you can search by state, province, or country, as well as by the practitioner's modality (acupuncture, chiropractic, Chinese herbs, etc.) and types of animals treated.

After you've gathered a few names and completed your initial screening by visiting their Web sites, you'll want to conduct an in-person interview with one or two practitioners. Call their office and explain that you are looking for a veterinarian and that you would like to visit their practice, take a tour of their facility, and chat briefly with the veterinarian. Don't be taken aback if you're told that you will have to pay for her time. Think of it as an investment in your dog's health.

Come prepared with questions and listen carefully to the answers, as they will strongly indicate whether or not you and the practitioner will be compatible. Some questions to ask include:

- If I feed my dog a raw food diet, are you going to refuse to treat him?
- What is your philosophy on yearly vaccine boosters?
- Do you believe in laboratory testing when my pet is ill?
- Do you believe in laboratory testing for annual wellness exams?
- Do you practice or consider alternative, holistic therapies?
- Do you refer to local specialists, including holistic veterinarians, if needed?

Consider building a relationship with a holistic veterinarian, if there is one in your area. Holistic veterinarians consider the "(w)hole" animal when making a diagnosis, including his lifestyle, nutrition, environment, emotional/social issues, and other factors. Holistic veterinarians are knowledgeable in both **allopathic** (conventional) and alternative/complementary forms of therapy, and can combine a variety of modalities to create an effective treatment plan. If there are no holistic veterinarians near you, seek out a conventional practitioner who is open-minded and knowledgeable about complementary and alternative therapies to accompany their regular practice.

Don't be bullied

Hopefully, if you have carefully screened potential veterinarians ahead of time, you will have found one that not only possesses excellent professional credentials, but who also treats you as a partner in your dog's health care. Such a veterinarian will respect your opinion and listen to your concerns and suggestions with an open mind. But, let's face it… we've all made poor relationship decisions in our lives!

The bottom line is that you should never have to feel uncomfortable with the way your veterinarian treats you. Yes, she is the expert. But, she does *not* know your dog like you do, and very often your knowledge and intuition will prove critical in solving your dog's health problem. If your veterinarian has an, "I'm the veterinarian, and what I say goes" attitude, then you are not in a relationship that will benefit your dog, and you need to find another health care partner.

This is serious business and could, in fact, be a matter of life or death. There is no place for egos when it comes to your dog's health. If your veterinarian is putting her ego before her desire to hear potentially valuable information from you, you should politely part ways and start fresh with someone who is more open-minded.

You must be the advocate for your dog. You must speak up for your dog, just as you would for your child. Trust your intuition. If you sense that something is not right with your pet, don't let an "expert" convince you that you are wrong. Stay on the "case" until you reach a satisfactory solution. Believe in yourself. Your canine companion is depending on you.

Pay attention to changes in your dog

One of the reasons it is so important to trust your instincts is that since you spend so much time with your dog, you may witness physical or behavioral changes in him that are not demonstrable during the short period when he visits the clinic. Recognizing these changes is critical so that you can pass the information along to your veterinarian. As we discussed in Chapter 4, keep a canine health journal and take video whenever you notice something that concerns you.

Remember, though, that when we are with someone everyday there is also the potential to *not* notice gradual changes that occur and even worsen over a long period of time. How about those dramatic changes in our own face and body that we are quite certain happened overnight? If a friend or family member visits who hasn't seen your dog in a while, ask if they notice anything different, either physically or behaviorally, about your dog. Don't dismiss their observations or comments. They could be on to a serious issue that you have overlooked.

Case study

Choco, a six-year-old, neutered male chocolate Labrador Retriever, had been an active competitor in agility and obedience trials until he suddenly became lazy, moody, lethargic, inattentive during competition events, and started gaining weight despite no increase in food consumption.

Choco's guardian had read about the relationship between behavioral changes, weight gain, and hypothyroidism, so he brought Choco to his veterinarian and asked for a checkup and blood tests for thyroid disease. The veterinarian said that this would be a waste of money, because Choco did not exhibit hair loss or skin disease. In fact, the veterinarian remarked on the excellent quality of Choco's skin and coat, and said that his weight gain was likely due to the lack of regular exercise to which he was accustomed.

Choco's guardian insisted on paying for the thyroid testing and, sure enough, he was right. Choco was severely hypothyroid and nearly 15 pounds overweight. No wonder he wasn't feeling well and was disinterested in his competitions and surroundings. Fortunately, with the proper diagnosis and treatment (thanks to a persistent guardian who trusted his instincts) Choco rapidly returned to his fit and trim normal weight, and was "flying" around the agility ring again in no time.

We're sure you can guess the moral of this story: You know your own dog best, so never give up until the correct diagnosis is found.

Take home points

- You must act as your dog's health care advocate.
- You have the power to make a substantial difference in your dog's health.
- All the knowledge in the world can't help your dog if you are afraid to trust your instincts.
- When researching, seek out the most accurate and up-to-date information.
- Use the Internet wisely, but cautiously, and you will have a treasure-trove of knowledge at your fingertips.
- Remember that friends mean well, but they are not experts. Take their advice with a grain of salt.
- Be a detective. Realize that even the seemingly smallest change in your dog's environment could be making him ill.

- Carefully screen potential veterinarians before entrusting your dog's health to their care.

- Don't let anyone bully you. If your veterinarian refuses to address your questions and concerns, politely sever the relationship and find someone who will.

- Pay attention to even the smallest physical or behavioral changes. Small changes can add up over time.

- And again: *You* are your dog's health care advocate. He is relying on you to speak up for him. Trust your instincts and don't give up. The health of your best friend depends on you!

Chapter 9

Case Studies

While we've scattered case studies throughout this book, we also wanted to dedicate an entire chapter to them in order to really illustrate the importance of identifying and treating thyroid disorder in dogs. The dogs featured below are lucky, since their guardians all did exactly what we have urged throughout this book. They followed their instincts and didn't give up on finding an answer to their dogs' health or behavioral problems—even when initial testing and the advice of their veterinarians appeared to prove them wrong.

Armed with the information in this book, you can now read these stories with the knowledge of a dog guardian who understands how to identify or rule out a thyroid condition in your canine companion. If there is one main take-away to all of these cases—and indeed this book—it's that the ultimate responsibility for our dogs' health rests on us, their caretakers. And although the results of some of these stories are still works in progress, these dogs are all receiving the best care possible thanks to guardians who trusted their "guts" in the face of adversity, and persevered in their quest to find an answer.

Read on and see if any of the stories below remind you of your own dog.

The headache and strange behavior case
Soshi, a four-year-old male Shiba Inu, was the top performing agility dog of his breed for the prior two years running. In fact, his performances were so superior that other competitors stopped entering against him. Then, one day, Soshi entered the tunnel of the agility course and refused to come out. When coaxed out he became somewhat submissive, only to repeat the same thing on a second try. His guardian had entered

him in several other trials and at each one Soshi did the same thing: He ran into the tunnel and refused to come out. Word soon got around that Soshi could lose in competition!

Soshi's guardian was devastated, and took him to her veterinarian for a checkup. Everything in the physical examination, blood, and urine tests appeared normal. Shortly thereafter, Soshi's guardian attended a seminar given by one of the authors (WJD) and learned about the vast array of behavioral issues associated with thyroid dysfunction. She even had a recent photo of Soshi to show. The photo was revealing. Soshi's eyes were squinting, his cheek muscles below both eyes were sunken in and, most noticeably, he appeared to be frowning as if he had a headache.

You know the answer: Soshi tested hypothyroid at the author's diagnostic laboratory!

It appeared that the bright sunlight bothered his eyes, causing him to squint and giving him what appeared to be a headache. Thyroid treatment was initiated, and just two weeks later Soshi was entered into another agility trial. His guardian decided to show him there because he already seemed to have perked up. Soshi swished through the course, ran through the tunnel and then proceeded to run through it again, while his disbelieving guardian and friends stared in amazement. His photo, while wearing a huge rosette that day, showed a normal, almond-eyed, happy dog. See Photos 28 and 29 in the insert.

The nurse, admit the patient case (showing all causative factors for autoimmune disease)

Carly, a two-and-a-half-year-old, intact female Irish Setter, was headed to the National Specialty show several hundred miles from her home. It was the heat of summertime. Carly had a history of recurring urinary tract infections, so her veterinarian recommended treating her with a potentiated sulfonamide antibiotic before the long trip, as a precaution. She had taken this antibiotic before to cure her urinary infection. He also gave her a combination vaccine booster, just in case she should "pick up" anything infectious at the show.

Carly was entered in obedience at the Specialty, but she came into heat unexpectedly just as they were leaving for the show and so she could not participate (bitches in heat cannot compete because it could disrupt the other competitors, especially the males). I (WJD) spoke the night before the show began and discussed various topics—including the four main factors, discussed elsewhere in this book—known to cause autoimmune disease, namely genetic predisposition, hormonal influences (especially of sex hormones), infections (especially of viruses and vaccines), and stress.

The next morning, I was observing the judging and noticed a female Irish setter behind me, lying stretched out on the grass with what appeared to be tiny purple spots on her underbelly. Rather than cause an uproar and disrupt judging, I quietly drew up beside the dog, lifted up her gums and earflaps, and checked her eye rims and under her tail. There were tiny purple spots (petechiae or pin-point hemorrhages) everywhere, and her vulva was swollen from the estrus. I quietly asked whose dog this was, at which point Carly's guardian appeared and started screaming. Needless to say, the judging was interrupted!

I attempted to calm her and told her that I would call for the show veterinarian. He turned out to be on call, so I called from a pay phone at the show site campgrounds (which was 95 degrees Fahrenheit by now). The person who answered indicated that the on-call veterinarian had been called away suddenly and had transferred the job to a nearby colleague. I then phoned the second veterinarian. I explained who I was and that we had an Irish Setter suffering from what I presumed was **thrombocytopenia**, a low platelet (thrombocyte) count, induced by one or more of sulfonamide antibiotic, vaccinations, and early estrus, and compounded by the high ambient temperature. I told him that we would bring her over immediately.

A friend drove Carly, her frantic guardian, and me to the clinic on a nearby highway. The young veterinarian met us at the door wearing a white lab coat and a stethoscope around his neck.

"Which one of you is Dr. Dodds," he asked? I stepped forward and extended my hand, only to have him appear to faint on the spot (I guess I scared him!). He quickly revived, and we proceeded inside to the examination room as I showed my colleague the petechiae.

At that point we needed to draw blood so that we could check Carly's complete blood counts (CBC), serum chemistry profile, and complete thyroid function. My colleague requested that I draw the blood, as he was too nervous. Once I filled the syringe with blood, some of which I placed in the tubes needed to prepare the serum for the chemistry and thyroid testing, I asked where their diagnostic lab was located. He told me that they didn't have one, and suggested I take the samples to the human hospital lab, which was located down the street.

We all packed back into the van as I held the syringe with the remaining blood to test the CBC. We parked in the circular driveway at the hospital entrance, and I asked everyone to wait while I went inside. I marched inside holding my syringe of blood and wearing street clothes (this was before the Federal regulations concerning blood safety and terrorism) and I introduced myself as "Dr. Jean Dodds, a hematologist from California." This, of course, was true, as I've studied and been responsible for both human and veterinary hematology. I just did not mention that I was a veterinarian. "I have a blood sample from a patient that I believe has sulfonamide-induced thrombocytopenia, and need a laboratory to confirm it," I explained.

"No problem, doctor," a nurse assured me. "We'll have someone here to help you right away."

Shortly thereafter, from a second floor stairway, entered a "Marcus Welby" look-alike in a white lab coat, his real name embroidered in red above the pocket. "Please come upstairs," he said. "I have two hematology resident students here and this will be an interesting case for them to review."

The CBC confirmed the diagnosis of thrombocytopenia. The four of us took turns looking under the binocular microscope and saw that there weren't many platelets present on Carly's blood smear. Her platelet count was around 35,000/cu mm, when the normal count for a dog is 175,000 - 400,000/cu mm. Before I could say anything, the doctor picked up the house phone and bellowed, "Nurse, admit the patient right away!"

I realized that I had some fast explaining to do!

"Please come and see the patient," I said to the three of them, "as she cannot easily be admitted here."

The puzzled doctor and his two residents followed me downstairs to the van, where I proceeded to introduce them to Carly. They were so amazed and intrigued—and looked her over carefully to see all the petechiae. They had never before been exposed to the "one medicine" concept—where animals share the same conditions and diseases, along with drug hypersensitivities—as humans.

We left on a high note. Carly was treated, first at my recommendation and then by her regular veterinarian, when she returned home. Her thyroid tests confirmed hypothyroidism, so she was successfully treated for it and would, of course, never take sulfonamides again.

While parts of this case are indeed humorous, it illustrates all four of the main causative factors that contribute to autoimmune disease.

The always "listen" to your dog case (more unusual behavior)

Kodak, a three-and-a-half-year-old, neutered Bearded Collie, was used to playing after school in the park with children and other dogs while his owner read or crocheted. Gradually, Kodak became withdrawn and hid under the park bench. He even refused to come out to play with the children and other dogs he used to love. Kodak's guardian was worried and took him to his veterinarian. When the veterinarian could find nothing wrong, he suggested that the dog could simply be "bored."

However, Kodak's behavioral issues worsened. His guardian would wake up at night to find Kodak standing at the foot of the bed, staring at her. This continued night after night until she could stand it no more. She realized that he was begging her to help him.

Kodak was referred to a university veterinary hospital, but after a physical examination, blood, and urine tests were performed, they also found nothing wrong with him.

Fortunately, his guardian did not give up, and she took him to see specialist veterinarians at two more university clinics. This, too, was to no avail, however. Then, one day, Kodak's guardian was talking to other Bearded Collie fanciers who told her they thought that Kodak had a thyroid disorder that was affecting his behavior. They then referred her to WJD.

Sure enough, once the thyroid antibody profile was performed via WJD's diagnostic laboratory, Kodak was confirmed to suffer from hypothyroidism.

After initiating thyroid therapy, Kodak regained his normal energy and behavior in short order, and he has remained well for more than five years.

Fortunately for Kodak, his guardian knew to trust her instincts and "listen" to her beloved dog rather than the veterinarians who insisted that nothing was wrong with him. See Photo 24 in the insert.

The combined bleeding disorder and thyroiditis case

Whisper, a three-year-old, intact female Doberman Pinscher, was diagnosed with autoimmune thyroiditis that included a very high T3 autoantibody (T3AA) level. In addition, she was found to be a carrier of von Willebrand disease (vWD), an inherited bleeding disorder very prevalent in this breed. Her dam died in midlife of chronic active hepatitis, also prevalent in the Doberman breed, and associated with excessive copper storage in the liver. Whisper's case history revealed that she had bled excessively from her gums at seven months of age, just before starting her maiden heat cycle. She had received a transfusion to stop the bleeding. Subsequently, she experienced pseudo-pregnancy, had an unstable temperament, and poor coat quality. She was bred once and reabsorbed the litter. Since Whisper was a working agility dog, her guardian elected to spay her.

Whisper continued bleeding after the spaying surgery. Her **hematocrit** (level of packed red blood cells) dropped from 42% to 28% and then further to 22%, at which point she was transfused and recovered uneventfully.

When Whisper was transfused as a puppy to control the bleeding gums, the test drawn after the transfusion showed that she had had normal von Willebrand factor activity. This result had been misleading, however, because the transfusion would have corrected her underlying vWD problem. Further, shortly after that time, a thyroid panel submitted to the Orthopedic Foundation of America (OFA) had been found to be normal.

Given these early results when Whisper was a puppy, the excessive bleeding from the spay surgery was not unexpected. However, the presence of concurrent autoimmune thyroiditis was a new wrinkle that likely aggravated her pre-existing clotting disorder.

This case illustrates that more than one problem can coexist in the same animal. In retrospect, the choice to spay Whisper was unwise without first waiting until thyroid therapy had corrected her thyroiditis. In addition, she should have received a transfusion ahead of time to lessen the risk of excessive surgical bleeding.

Whisper's case emphasizes the importance of rechecking thyroid profiles on a regular basis until midlife or even later. Note how her normal OFA thyroid result from when she had been an adolescent became significantly abnormal once she became a young adult.

The fearful puppy and aggressive adult case

Churchill, a three-year-old, neutered male English Springer Spaniel, had been provoked by a nine-year-old child who had been hitting him with a branch. Churchill reacted by biting the child. His history as a puppy included fearful behavior. Attempts to rehabilitate him by obedience classes with positive reinforcement "clicker" training—which was intended to build confidence and strengthen his bond with his family—had not been successful. He was primarily kept in the yard and had been crated when younger, because he would urinate on the spot when anyone would reach for him. He also exhibited aggressive behavior when made to do things he didn't want to do, such as get a bath or go into his crate. After the bite incident, Churchill was quarantined at a local dog-training kennel. He did not exhibit any signs of aggression there, but he also was not being provoked.

A thyroid antibody panel was performed at the diagnostic laboratory of WJD. Sure enough, Churchill was found to be significantly hypothyroid. Thyroxine therapy was initiated twice daily and his behavioral training continued.

This was a difficult case, because Churchill began exhibiting behavioral abnormalities as a pre-pubertal puppy and the family had unintentionally reinforced these behaviors.

However, a happy outcome occurred once Churchill's hypothyroidism was corrected. His confidence was restored and his behavioral reactivity gradually lessened. He is now a relaxed and sociable companion for the family and a cheerful playmate for the kids.

The noise and motion-phobic, overweight pet case

Percy, a four-year-old, neutered male Australian Shepherd mix, had previously been diagnosed as hypothyroid and had a long-term history of behavioral issues. Treatment with thyroid hormone had not significantly alleviated his behavioral problems. Three separate dog trainers had tried to stabilize his temperament. Percy seemed to be in a constant state of stress, and was always on alert and ready to attack. He remained overweight, despite two years of treatment for hypothyroidism. He became out of breath very quickly when exercising and he was compulsive around anything metal. He licked his chain collar and leash for hours on end.

When anyone in the home moved toward or opened the dishwasher, he became very aggressive towards the machine. He also hated the vacuum cleaner and would attack his bed if anyone tried to touch it. He was startled by sudden noises, and since the home was on the flight path of a local airport, whenever a plane flew over, he grabbed a stuffed toy and shook it aggressively.

Perhaps the most troubling issue for the family was that when somebody sneezed, Percy would grab one of his dog toys and try to rip it apart. He had bitten family members on several occasions, although not severely. When doing so, it seemed that he just "snapped" and was in such a state that he could not control himself. He would then go into a spell or trance, and after a few minutes would become normal again.

Obviously, this poor dog had a major problem with noise phobias and redirected aggression. His dose of thyroxine for his weight was deemed correct based on his follow-up thyroid panel, which showed that he was adequately supplemented. Two additional approaches were recommended, namely using melatonin twice daily to try to control his noise phobia and anxiety tendencies, and secondly, lavender aromatherapy was used to help him calm down. Dried lavender sachets were placed around the areas he frequented, lavender chips were placed within his dog bed, and lavender aerosol spray was used where he slept.

Follow-up two months later with the family indicated that Percy was doing much better and was less reactive during situations of stress or loud unexpected noises. He had also regained his svelte figure.

The case of the persistent guardian

Tootsie Roll, a two-year-old spayed, female Airedale Terrier, gained 20 pounds in the course of a year and suffered from unilateral hair loss. A routine thyroid profile at the local veterinary clinic revealed that Tootsie Roll had a very good level of T4 and free T4. However, her guardian had read that weight gain and hair loss could indicate hypothyroidism, so she decided that more complete thyroid testing was needed. She took her dog to a holistic veterinary clinic. At that clinic, where thyroid testing was routinely performed by WJD's laboratory, the T4 and free T4 levels were found to be very good, but the T3 and free T3 were both elevated to nearly double the upper limit of the normal ranges. The thyroglobulin autoantibody (TgAA) level was equivocal, meaning that it was not low enough to be normal or high enough to be clearly positive.

Tootsie Roll's very high T3 and free T3 levels, along with the equivocal TgAA, suggested that she had a circulating T3 autoantibody (T3AA) which had spuriously raised her T3 and free T3 levels. This also provided an explanation for her weight gain and hair loss. A follow-up T3AA assay was performed and was also positive.

After six months of thyroxine therapy, Tootsie Roll was back to her old self. She lost weight, her hair grew back, and she acted like a puppy again.

This case illustrates the importance of following up suspect cases with a complete thyroid autoantibody profile when routine thyroid testing appears normal. It was the persistence of Tootsie Roll's caring guardian that in this case led to the correct diagnosis.

The apparent inhalant allergy case

Roxey, a two-year-old, spayed female fawn-and-white Boxer, was a rescue dog that had been plagued with chronic allergy symptoms. The referring veterinary dermatologist diagnosed **atopic** (inhalant) allergies. Roxey had sore, weepy, yeasty ears, horrible **pododermatitis** (red, itchy feet) with oozing blisters that she licked constantly, and episodes of hives all over her trunk. She rubbed her ears continuously on rugs to get some relief from the itching, which further aggravated the soreness and irritation. Her coat texture and quality were good, except for the hives. She had also started to gain weight and displayed a frenetic behavior.

The veterinary dermatologist performed laboratory testing, which included a CBC, serum chemistry profile, and T4 test. Nothing unusual was found, except for high **neutrophil** and **monocyte** counts (the white blood cells associated with inflammation), and a high **globulin** level (the antibodies the body makes in response to ongoing inflammation). In addition, Roxey's T4 level was low-normal. The dermatologist prescribed an **autogenous bacterin product**, a mixture of material taken from the infected sores of her own body, and grown in a laboratory with an immune stimulant. He gave her weekly injections of the product, like a vaccine, in an attempt to make her immune to the organisms that caused her condition. He also gave Roxey injections of long-acting corticosteroids and suggested a diet change to a prescription diet for allergic dogs.

When Roxey's veterinarian retested her six weeks later, her white blood cell counts showed little improvement over the prior results, and her liver enzymes were very high. In addition, her T4 level was very low. She also hated the new prescription food. Roxey's guardian decided that the drugs were harming her, so he sought my (WJD) opinion.

I decided to start over from the beginning and run a more complete thyroid profile, which showed significant hypothyroidism and elevated TgAA.

Thyroxine supplementation was prescribed for Roxey's optimum weight, to be administered twice daily, apart from meals. I also switched her to a limited-antigen source grain-free food and treats. I stopped her steroid and autogenous bacterin injections and replaced them for the short-term with trimeprazine-prednisolone (Temaril-P®, Pfizer), at the minimum dose needed to control her itching and hives. I treated her ears and feet with a 1% miconazole cream (Monistat 7®—DuoPack, McNeil-PPC) to control the yeast. I also prescribed a gentamicin-betamethasone (Gentocin® Topical Spray, Schering-Plough) spray to be used on her feet whenever a new blister lesion appeared.

Six weeks later, Roxey was a "new" dog. She had lost four pounds, had a waist again, and was much calmer. Her ears and feet no longer had an odor and she wasn't scratching and licking her feet. Also, her hives were gone. Laboratory tests still showed elevated liver enzymes, but they were at about half the previous levels. Roxey's guardian was concerned, but I assured him that it would likely take another four-to-six weeks for all of her lab tests to normalize. Sure enough, on the next recheck visit, all CBC and serum chemistry lab results were normal, her thyroid levels were perfect for post-thyroxine expectations, and her TgAA was once again within normal limits.

This case teaches us to correct the underlying thyroid imbalance, when present, and to change the diet and treats to grain-free, home cooked, or raw. Other environmental exposures should also be minimized, including vaccines (other than rabies as required by law) and preventive medicines for heartworm, fleas, and ticks, if warranted where you live.

The untreated thyroiditis case

Tipster, a four-and-a-half-year-old, 75-pound male Golden Retriever, was first diag-nosed in February 2008 as having **positive compensatory thyroiditis**, the early stage of the disease where thyroid hormone levels are still normal, but thyroid autoantibod-ies are elevated. Although his TgAA was 212% on the screening test and 189% on the confirmatory test (normal ranges are < 35% and <10%, respectively), his T4 and free T4 were just at the lower end of the optimal ranges. The endocrinologist at the refer-ence lab indicated that Tipster did not need thyroxine therapy at that time because he was not showing typical signs of hypothyroidism.

Tipster's thyroid profile was retested at the same reference lab the following year, as his guardian noted that he exhibited less stamina on tracking and other field events, and that he tired easily. In May 2009, his T4 was clearly suboptimal and the free T4 was below the lower limit of the lab reference range. The TgAA was 71% on the screening test and 62% on the confirmatory test. Despite the low free T4, the endocrinologist stated that, "circulating concentrations of thyroid hormones and thyroid stimulating hormone are generally normal, indicating adequate thyroid function. It is unlikely that this dog is hypothyroid at present, but there is increased risk of hypothyroidism in the future." Nothing was mentioned about starting thyroxine therapy with the persistently high TgAA and lowered thyroid hormone levels!

In early 2010, Tipster began having seizures, seemingly out of the blue. He started phenobarbital therapy after three seizures occurred that February. He had still not received any thyroxine therapy. His repeat thyroid profile showed similar thyroid hor-mone levels as the prior year, a screening TgAA of 97% and a confirmatory TgAA of 121%. These levels had climbed again since the 2009 profile. A serum chemistry profile and the phenobarbital level were all within expected norms.

With his persistently high TgAA, Tipster should have been taking thyroxine supple-mentation all along. Once he started having seizures, it was even more important that he began the thyroxine immediately, since thyroiditis and hypothyroidism can trigger seizure disorders. He should have continued the phenobarbital at least until his thy-roiditis resolved on thyroxine therapy.

On my (WJD) advice, Tipster was started on thyroxine at 0.5 mg twice daily (brand name product preferred over generic), with the medication given apart from meals, at least one hour before or three hours after each meal to assure absorption. This was a conservative dose for his weight.

Until the thyroiditis had been properly addressed, we did not recommend vaccinating him, especially for rabies, given his thyroiditis and seizure disorder. Only healthy dogs should receive vaccinations, when needed. Furthermore, as a properly vaccinated adult dog, Tipster did not require any vaccines other than rabies, once he regained his health. Vaccine titers could be measured against distemper and parvovirus every three years, if his guardian desired.

As of this writing, Tipster is doing better on thyroxine therapy, and has had only one mild seizure in the last three months. The plan now is to start weaning him gradually off the phenobarbital to determine whether the thyroiditis alone was responsible for the seizures or whether he also has epilepsy.

The here's why we don't give thyroxine with food case

Zachary, a 10-year-old, neutered, 71-pound male Labrador Retriever, had been taking thyroxine for hypothyroidism that was first diagnosed when he was two years old. His guardian had been baffled at the low thyroid test results back then, as he had been very skinny and had had a shiny coat. Nevertheless, I (WJD) convinced her to try thyroxine therapy, and Zachary was started on 0.3 mg thyroxine administered twice daily.

He did very well, but gradually over the years his thyroxine dose was increased based just on sub-optimal T4 levels post-pill. By the time Zachary was 10 years old, the dose was up to 0.6 mg given twice daily, even though he was now geriatric and had lost weight. His thyroid test results, which were run at two different reference labs, showed T4 and free T4 levels barely within the lower limit of the reference ranges, although his TSH was very low (as expected for dogs receiving appropriate thyroid supplement) and his TgAA was normal, also as expected.

The local veterinarian wanted to increase the thyroxine dose yet again, to 0.8 mg twice daily, based merely on the suboptimal T4 and free T4 levels. He did not take into account the expected low TSH level for a dog receiving thyroxine, nor Zachary's current weight or age.

Zachary's guardian was reluctant to increase the dose of thyroxine, so she started adding a natural thyroid support extract to his regimen. A recheck four weeks later of just the T4 found that it had dropped even lower!

At this point, Zachary's guardian contacted me again and asked me what she should do.

I knew that something was amiss and I asked her several questions, including: Was he at his optimum weight or was he thin? Was he eating a kibble, raw, or homemade diet? Did she supplement his diet with kelp or other iodine sources? Did she give the thyroxine with meals? Were these tests run at four-to-six hours post-pill? The answer was revealed in a flash: Zachary ate a raw diet, and the thyroxine had always been given with his meals!

Zachary's thyroxine dose was lowered to 0.5 mg administered twice daily for his age and current weight—and given *apart* from meals. Follow-up testing a month later revealed that his T4 and free T4 levels were in the upper half of the lab reference ranges. Everyone was happy, including the clinical veterinarian who had no idea of the importance of giving thyroxine apart from meals!

The thin dog with thyroiditis case

Talbot, an eighteen-month-old, intact male English Setter, weighed only 41 pounds, but also lacked an appetite. He had a good temperament and carried good coat length and quality. A thyroid profile was requested, because thyroiditis is so prevalent in this breed. The results were normal, except for a very high TgAA. The reference lab endocrinologist diagnosed "compensatory autoimmune thyroiditis," but recommended that Talbot not be treated with thyroxine until such time that the thyroid levels (T4 and freeT4) became abnormal.

Talbot continued refusing to eat enough and he continued to lose weight. He became grumpy and failed to pay attention to commands during agility competition. Finally, when Talbot was three years old, he was retested at Hemopet's lab. Sure enough, his T4 and freeT4 were both found to be sub-optimal and his TgAA level had climbed to 121%. Treatment with thyroxine at 0.3 mg twice daily was initiated immediately.

Most clinical veterinarians do not expect a dog with thyroid disorder to be very thin and to display a poor appetite. They're taught to watch for weight gain, bilaterally symmetrical hair loss, and dislike of the cold. What they're not taught is that these signs do not typically appear until at least 70% of the dog's thyroid gland has been damaged or destroyed by the gradual progression of this disorder. In the early inflammatory stages of the disease process, signs like those exhibited by Talbot are common.

The big overdose of thyroxine case

Cyndi, a 10-year-old, spayed, 114-pound female Golden Retriever, had been taking thyroxine for hypothyroidism that was first diagnosed at four years of age. Her guardian had been battling Cyndi's weight gain for the previous three years. Cyndi had gained nearly 30 pounds on a restricted diet of low calorie, low fat commercial kibble supplemented with green beans and small amounts of chicken. She ate less than 1.5 cups of kibble twice daily, and received no treats.

Cyndi's local veterinarian regularly retested her thyroxine (T4) level. Since he repeatedly found it to be low, he continued to increase the thyroxine dose until she was taking a whopping 1.5 mg of thyroxine twice daily. That dosage should have been enough for a 250 pound dog! Cyndi's guardian came to see me (WJD) to have Cyndi's thyroid profile rechecked and to discuss her diet and weight issues. With the last increase in the thyroxine dose from 1.0 to 1.5 mg twice daily, Cyndi developed a series of **"hot spots"** (moist dermatitis) and blackened pigmentation to her skin in her **perineum** (the area around and below the anus), inner thighs, and vulvar area.

Before receiving Cyndi's lab test results, I explained to the client that massive doses of thyroxine can either result in lowered thyroid analytes (because the drug is excreted faster to avoid thyrotoxicosis) or that it could reveal very high levels (if her metabolism was unable to utilize and excrete the drug).

The results were amazingly high (see below):

Thyroid analyte	Units	Cyndi	Normal reference ranges
T4	µg/dL	10.1	0.80-3.80
FreeT4	ng/dL	5.70	0.55-2.32
T3	ng/dL	158	30-70
Free T3	pg/mL	4.6	1.6-3.5

Because these levels were all so high, Cyndi's thyroxine dose had to be lowered gradually. The first cut was to go down to 1.0 mg of thyroxine twice daily for 10 days; then to 0.8 mg twice daily for four weeks. After that period, her thyroid profile was to be rechecked and adjusted downwards again, if the recheck levels were still too high. Sure enough, her thyroid levels were still too high, and so her thyroxine was cut back to 0.6 mg twice daily. The best news was that Cyndi finally started to lose weight, even though her thyroxine dose was lowered. At the time of this writing, four months later, she had lost 25 pounds and was doing well on 0.6 mg of thyroxine given twice daily.

The situation described above for Cyndi is quite commonly also seen with Sighthounds that are often overdiagnosed with hypothyroidism and then overdosed with thyroxine, either because the veterinarian was unaware that Sighthounds normally have lower basal thyroid levels and require lesser amounts of thyroxine replacement therapy, or that the breed belonged to the Sighthound class.

What is important about this case is that it is inappropriate to keep increasing the dose of thyroid supplement based on a T4 test alone. Moreover, if the dose used far exceeds the expected therapeutic amount for the dog's weight, something is wrong metabolically.

Final words

We hope that you have gained as much from reading this book as we have from writing it. As we said in the beginning, if even one dog lives a healthier, happier, longer life because of this information, then we are very grateful.

Our dogs give us everything they have: undivided attention, endless loyalty, and unconditional love. At the same time, they rely on us to look out for them, to speak up for them, and to do what is right for them. We are their voice. We are their advocates. And when it comes to their health, we are often their only hope.

You now have the knowledge to make a huge impact on your dog's health and quality of life. If you use this knowledge and trust your instincts, you and your canine friend will be on the road to a long and happy life together. Enjoy!

Appendix A

Autoimmune diseases (also called immune-mediated diseases) are caused by the failure of self-tolerance. A schematic flow chart of how these diseases arise is shown in Chapter 2, Figure 3. The autoimmune diseases most commonly seen in the canine population are discussed here by body system. Any breed or mixed breed can be affected.

Endocrine system

Thyroid gland/Thyroiditis. Autoimmune thyroiditis is a self-directed immune reaction within the thyroid gland, where the affected individual's **lymphocytes** (white blood cells that convey or regulate immunity) progressively destroy the thyroid gland. See Chapter 1 for more details.

Thyroiditis affects a wide variety of dog breeds.

Adrenal glands/Addison's disease. Addison's disease results when the adrenal glands are underactive and do not produce enough adrenal hormones. The primary form of Addison's disease is a self-directed immune reaction within the adrenal glands, where the affected individual's lymphocytes progressively destroy these glands.

The result is insufficient production of either **cortisol**, the steroid hormone that determines how the body handles stress, helps regulate how the body uses nutrients, and helps maintain proper cardiovascular functions, or **aldosterone**, the hormone that helps to regulate blood pressure and allows the kidneys to maintain a proper water-to-salt balance in the body.

This disease can cause many serious health issues, and is often misdiagnosed as another disease. The symptoms of Addison's disease mimic other general conditions, such as fatigue, diarrhea, sweating, and muscle pain. When combined with autoimmune thyroid disease, the condition is called **Schmidt's syndrome.** Once diagnosed, the treatment options for Addison's disease are very effective, but will require your dog to take medication for the rest of his life.

There are two different classifications for Addison's disease—primary and secondary. In primary adrenal insufficiency, the disease is caused by improper function or damage to the adrenal glands. In secondary Addison's disease, the adrenal glands are still functioning normally. Impaired adrenal function can be seen with the following:

- Adrenal dysgenesis, a rare genetic condition in which the adrenal glands are not formed properly during fetal development.

- Impaired steroidogenesis, where the adrenal gland cannot form cortisol normally because of inadequate delivery of cholesterol to the adrenals, which is needed to form steroid hormones.

- Adrenal destruction by immune-mediated attack; prolonged use of steroid hormones.

- A damaged or dysfunctional pituitary gland, which reduces the output of the ACTH (adrenocorticotropic hormone) necessary for regulating cortisol production deficiency of aldosterone, which produces a drop in blood pressure and severe dehydration.

Classical symptoms of Addison's disease are non-specific and include:

- Muscle weakness and general lethargy (listlessness), in which affected dogs are unable to jump up on the couch or bed, have trouble climbing stairs, frequently lie down, or display a lack of enthusiasm for activities involving physical exertion.

- Vomiting and diarrhea, sometimes with blood present.

- Hyperpigmentation, shown as small patches or spots of darker skin around the armpits, mucous membranes, or inside the cheek.

- Joint pain, which may manifest as whimpering or yelping during walking, or as a limp.

- Poor appetite.

- Shivering or muscle tremors.

Predisposed breeds include: the Alaskan Klee Kai; Bearded Collie; English Setter; Eurasier; Great Dane; Labradoodle; Leonberger; Nova Scotia Duck Tolling Retriever; Old English Sheepdog; Pharaoh Hound; Portuguese Water Dog; Soft-Coated Wheaten Terrier; Standard Poodle; and Weimaraner. Addison's disease is more common in females, and in young or middle-aged adults.

Pancreas/juvenile diabetes mellitus. A self-directed immune reaction within the pancreas, where the affected individual's lymphocytes progressively destroy this gland.

As with humans, diabetes mellitus occurs in animals when the pancreas doesn't produce enough **insulin** (the hormone required for the body to efficiently utilize sugars, fats, and proteins). This disease most commonly occurs in middle-aged to older female dogs and in male cats, but can also occasionally afflict younger animals. The juvenile form is usually heritable and so can also occur in other family members.

Dogs who are overweight or have **pancreatitis** (inflammation of the pancreas) are predisposed to diabetes. Certain drugs that interfere with insulin—such as excessive or prolonged use of corticosteroids and hormones used to prevent estrus—can also increase the likelihood of diabetes. The most common clinical and laboratory signs of diabetes in dogs include:

- Constant hunger
- Excessive drinking and urination
- Very high blood and urine glucose levels
- Weight loss due to the body's improper use of dietary nutrients
- Chronic infections of the skin, bladder, and kidney
- Cataracts in the eyes

The diagnosis of diabetes is made by finding a large increase in glucose levels in the blood and also spilling over into the urine.

Predisposed breeds include: the Alaskan Malamute; Finnish Spitz; Keeshond; Schipperke; and Toy and Miniature Poodles. Juvenile diabetes is more common in females.

Hematologic (blood)

A self-directed immune reaction within the bone marrow and blood cells, whereby the affected individual's lymphocytes progressively destroy one or more blood cell lines (red blood cells, white blood cells, and platelets).

The classical clinical signs are:

- Anemia and **icterus** (jaundice), when the red blood cells are destroyed, or anemia secondary to blood loss when the platelets are destroyed
- Tiny **petechiae** (pin-point hemorrhages)
- **Ecchymoses** (patchy hemorrhages) or mucosal surface bleeding, when platelets are affected, and recurrent infections when the white blood cells are destroyed (a rare condition)

Erythrocytes/immune-mediated or autoimmune hemolytic anemia.

- Spayed females are overrepresented
- The most commonly affected breed is the American Cocker Spaniel

- Other predisposed breeds include: the Akita; Collie; English Springer Spaniel; Kerry Blue Terrier; Labrador Retriever; Long Haired Dachshund; Miniature Schnauzer; Old English Sheepdog; Shih Tzu; Standard Poodle; and Vizsla.

- Up to two-thirds of affected dogs also have immune-mediated thrombocytopenia (Evan's Syndrome).

- Many affected breeds are also hypothyroid or have thyroiditis.

- Triggers of the disease include: recent vaccinations, drug use (sulfonamides, estrogens), chemical or toxic exposure, surgery, hormonal change, injury, infection, and stress.

Platelets (immune-mediated thrombocytopenia, ITP).

- The majority of chronic ITP cases are immune-mediated.

- Overrepresented breeds include: the Akita; American Cocker Spaniel; Kerry Blue Terrier; Long Haired Dachshund; Old English Sheepdog; Samoyed; Shih Tzu; Standard Poodle; Vizsla; Weimaraner; and other white and dilute coat-color breeds.

- Up to one-third of affected dogs also suffer from immune-mediated hemolytic anemia (Evan's Syndrome).

- ITP is characterized by **microthrombocytosis** (small platelet size) on blood smears (Mean Platelet Volume (MPV) < 5.4 fl).

- Many affected dogs are also hypothyroid or have thyroiditis.

- Triggers of the disease include: recent vaccinations, drug use (sulfonamides, estrogens), chemical or toxic exposure, surgery, hormonal change, injury, infection, and stress.

Case study

Dolly, a six-year-old, intact female Old English Sheepdog, was due for her booster vaccinations in mid-summer in order to prepare her for breeding. She came into estrus several days later, and five days later she collapsed. She was rushed to a veterinary teaching hospital with a packed cell volume (PCV) of 6% (normal levels are 35-55%), and diagnosed with autoimmune hemolytic anemia (AIHA; also called IMHA for immune–mediated hemolytic anemia) and immune-mediated thrombocytopenia (ITP). When these two autoimmune diseases appear together, the combination is called Evan's syndrome.

Dolly was very ill and was transfused twice, but not expected to live. Her bone marrow was non-regenerative and she was diagnosed with bone marrow failure. Taken back home to die, her owner contacted WJD and a protocol of combined immunosuppressive therapy with corticosteroids, cyclosporine, and azathioprine was initiated. This was accompanied by transfusions of **universal donor canine packed red blood cells** (compatible with all dogs, regardless of their blood type), a **hematinic** (an agent that acts to increase the amount of hemoglobin in the blood) to provide the nutrients essential for new blood cell production, and a thyroid supplement to stimulate the bone marrow.

Interestingly, another piece of the diagnostic puzzle was identified when Dolly had a complete thyroid antibody profile measured, because her thyroid function was abnormal and her blood sample had elevated thyroid autoantibodies. For this second reason, thyroid supplementation was deemed essential.

After adding thyroxine to her therapy, Dolly started a miraculous recovery. Once she was fully recovered, she was spayed during anestrus. The four main causative factors that contributed to her collapse and autoimmune disease were a genetic predisposition (breed at high risk), hormonal influences (especially of sex hormones, Dolly was in estrus), infections (especially of viruses, Dolly was vaccinated with a combo MLV booster vaccine), and stress (high ambient temperature and humidity).

Muscles

Myasthenia Gravis. In the acquired form, this is a self-directed neuromuscular immune reaction within the muscles, where the affected individual's lymphocytes progressively destroy this tissue.

The primary sign is weakness, as this disease is due to an inability of certain nerve receptors (acetylcholine receptors) to function properly. This prevents the stimulus for muscles to contract, which leads to the weak appearance. In older dogs, the first sign may be **megaesophagus** (enlargement of the esophagus due to muscular weakness), leading to esophageal flabbiness and swallowing difficulties. This can cause regurgitation and lead to inhalation pneumonia.

Predisposed breeds include: the English Springer Spaniel; German Shepherd; Golden Retriever; Parson's Jack Russell Terrier; and Smooth Fox Terriers.

Dermatomyositis (DM). A self-directed immune reaction within the dermal layer of the skin and surrounding muscles, where the affected individual's lymphocytes progressively destroy these tissues.

In dogs, this is an inherited inflammatory condition that involves the skin, muscle, and sometimes, the blood vessels. The predominant theory is that DM is an autoimmune disease, inherited as an **autosomal** (where both sexes are affected) dominant trait, where the degree of abnormality is inherited in a variable way among the offspring.

The tissues most commonly affected are the skin (dermatitis on the face, ears, tail tip, and over the bony parts of the distal extremities) and then the muscles (myositis, which can be subtle to severe). Usually the **temporal** (head) and **masseter** (jaw) muscles are involved. More severe cases can result in generalized muscle disease and involve the esophageal muscles.

It is most prevalent in the Collie and Shetland Sheepdog, as well as related crossbreeds.

Masticatory muscle myositis (MMM). A self-directed immune reaction within the **mastication** (chewing) muscles in the jaw, where the affected individual's lymphocytes progressively destroy this tissue.

This is an inflammatory condition involving immune-mediated destruction of masticatory muscle fibers. Young and middle-aged dogs are most commonly affected. The disease can develop in either **acute** (sudden) form (as in post-vaccination of puppies) or **chronic** (long-term) form. The chronic form is more common.

Clinical signs include:

- Swelling associated with facial and forehead muscles
- Fever
- Pain upon opening the mouth
- Reluctance to eat or chew
- Excessive salivation
- Bulging of the eyes
- **Prolapse** (protrusion) of the **third eyelids** (the membrane that is found in the inner corner of each eye and can spread out over the eye when needed to protect it from harm)
- Shrinkage of head muscles

MMM affects many breeds including: German Shepherds; Doberman Pinschers; Retrievers; and especially toys like the Cavalier King Charles Spaniel.

Polymyositis. A self-directed inflammatory reaction within the muscles, where the affected individual's lymphocytes progressively destroy this tissue.

This is a **systemic** (affecting the entire body), noninfectious (probably immune-mediated) inflammatory muscle disorder found in adult dogs. It may display as either acute or chronic and progressive. Clinical signs include depression, lethargy, weakness, weight loss, lameness, **myalgia** (muscle pain), and muscle atrophy.

Laboratory findings may reveal high or very high creatine kinase enzyme levels. Muscle biopsy reveals muscle **necrosis** (death of living cells or tissues), infiltration of muscle by immunologically active white blood cells (lymphocytes and plasma cells), and muscle fiber regeneration.

Polymyositis may also be associated with megaesophagus and other immune-mediated disorders (myasthenia gravis, systemic lupus erythematosus, and polyarthritis). Prognosis is favorable, with therapy, although relapses can occur.

Predisposed breeds include the Golden Retriever and Newfoundland.

Joints (rheumatoid arthritis)

A self-directed immune reaction within the joints, where the affected individual's lymphocytes progressively destroy the joints. The condition is believed to be due to deposition of immune complexes in the **synovia** (joint capsules).

Rheumatoid Arthritis is rare in dogs.

Eyes

Keratoconjunctivitis Sicca ("Dry Eye" or KCS). A self-directed immune reaction within the **conjunctiva** (surface of the eye), where the affected individual's lymphocytes progressively destroy this surface layer of the eyes.

KCS results in inadequate tear production. The causes can include injuries to the tear glands or their nerves, eye infections, reactions to drugs such as sulfonamides, accidental surgical removal during third eyelid surgery, and an immune-mediated reaction within the tear glands.

Symptoms include development of a thick, yellowish discharge over the eye or eyes. Without the bactericidal tears that normally bathe the eyes, secondary eye infections are common. Since the eye is unprotected, dust and pollens can accumulate. Diagnosis is made by checking tear production with a small piece of absorbent material called a Schirmer tear test strip. When placed in the eye, the tears soak and migrate up the strip. The wet area of the strip is then measured and compared to the expected normal values.

Dry Eye occurs in many dog breeds, and is associated with thyroiditis especially in the American Cocker Spaniel. Other predisposed breeds include: the English Bulldog; Lhasa Apso; Miniature Schnauzer; Pekingese; Shih Tzu; Soft-coated Wheaten Terrier and Toy or Miniature Poodle.

Case study

Priscilla, a four-year-old, intact female American Cocker Spaniel, developed excessive tearing of both eyes that began as a clear discharge and progressed to a sticky greenish discharge around the eye rims. She had also experienced recurring eye infections, her eyes appeared dry and dull, and she frequently blinked. Her nostrils developed crusty, dry borders on the outer edges.

Priscilla's owners took her to the veterinarian, where a diagnosis of dry eye (KCS) was made based on the clinical evaluation and results of the Schirmer Tear Test that measures the amount of tear production. KCS has been associated with immune-mediated diseases and recent viral infections, such as with canine distemper.

Priscilla's owners contacted her breeder, who recommended doing a complete thyroid function work-up because of the known association of KCS with hypothyroidism in the breed. In fact, since close relatives of Priscilla had been diagnosed with thyroid disease, this made very good sense. Sure enough, testing showed that Priscilla did have heritable autoimmune thyroiditis. Treatment alleviated the dry eye and stopped further progression of the destruction of her thyroid gland.

Uveitis/Anterior uveitis. A self-directed immune reaction within the **uvea** (the anterior part of the eyes), where the affected individual's lymphocytes progressively destroy this tissue.

Anterior uveitis is inflammation that affects the **anterior** (front) part of the eye, which is the dark tissue of the eye that contains blood vessels. The iris, the tissue that makes up the pupil, is also typically involved, but the **posterior** (back) part of the eye may not be affected. Anterior uveitis affects many breeds.

Pannus (Chronic Superficial Keratitis). An immune-mediated corneal disease of both eyes, in which ultraviolet light and altitude (both high and low) influence the severity of the disease. It is a progressive, non-painful, inflammatory disease of the cornea, conjunctiva, and sometimes the third eyelids. Characteristic signs are variable pigmentation of the eyes, **vascularization** (increased number of corneal blood vessels), the presence of granulation tissue, and cholesterol deposits.

The corneal changes usually begin on the lower outside surface of the eye. Some dogs also have dry eye (KCS) problems. As the disease progresses, blindness can develop. Autoimmune factors and genetic predisposition play a part.

Pannus affects many breeds. It is most commonly found in the German Shepherd, but also in: the Border Collie; Dachshund; Greyhound; Husky; Labrador Retriever; and Poodle.

Uveodermatologic Syndrome (VKH; Vogt-Koyanagi-Harada Syndrome). A condition seen in humans and dogs involving various organs in the body that contain **melanocytes** (melanin-producing cells). It is characterized by uveitis (see above), **poliosis** (whitening of hair), **vitiligo** (loss of pigment in the skin), and, rarely, meningitis. In dogs, VKH syndrome most commonly affects young animals. The uveitis usually occurs first and is often severe enough to cause blindness. VKH syndrome can progress to cause retinal detachment, cataracts, and glaucoma. Skin lesions include loss of pigment and hair on the eyelids, nose, and lips. Animals displaying these symptoms can be confirmed by tissue biopsy. The prognosis is poor and outcome extremely serious.

Predisposed breeds include: the Akita Inu; Alaskan Malamute; Chow-Chow; Samoyed; Siberian Husky; and Tosa Inu.

Skin
Pemphigus Disorders. Potentially severe autoimmune conditions of the skin and mucous membranes.

Like the parallel human disorder, canine pemphigus causes blistering eruptions primarily affecting the face, ears, and mouth. Several subtypes exist, namely pemphigus foliaceus, pemphigus vulgaris, pemphigus erythematosus (head and feet; commonly test antinuclear antibody positive) and pemphigus vegetans (warty growths). Pemphigus foliaceus is the most common type seen in dogs, with pemphigus vulgaris ranked second.

Predisposed breeds include: the Akita Inu; Collie; and Shetland Sheepdog.

Systemic Lupus Erythematosus (SLE). An autoimmune disease, characterized by a specific antibody or cell-mediated immune response against the body's own tissues.

Systemic lupus affects many organs and is a life-threatening disease. Because antibodies are produced against a variety of organs, clinical signs vary with the organs that are affected. Often, severe damage occurs in the kidneys and blood vessels. In other cases, the red blood cells are attacked and destroyed, which causes anemia.

Predisposed breeds include: the German Shepherd; Collie; Shetland Sheepdog; Shih Tzu; Standard Poodle; and Vizsla.

Vitiligo. A hereditary skin disease that is not noticeable at birth. Affected young dogs develop bleached splotches of skin that occasionally also affect the hair coat and paw pads. Most splotches are on the face, especially the bridge of the muzzle or around the eyes. Similar patches also appear on mucous membranes inside the mouth and nostrils, around the anus and genitals, and in the retina of the eyes. The hair that grows on affected areas may turn white. Affected areas may repigment, remain unchanged, or wax and wane. The full extent of the depigmentation usually occurs within three-to-six months of the onset of disease.

When vitiligo affects only the nose, dog breeders sometimes refer to it as "snow nose." Sometimes depigmentation only affects the bridge of the nose and the adjacent muzzle areas. Breeders have dubbed this "Dudley nose."

A marked breed predisposition exists for the Belgian Tervuren. Other predisposed breeds include: the Dachshund; Doberman Pinscher; German Shepherd; German Shorthaired Pointer; Old English Sheepdog; Rottweiler; and Vizsla.

Kidneys
Immune-Complex Glomerulonephritis. An immune-complex disease caused by deposition of antigen-antibody complexes in the **subendothelial** (below the surface lining of blood vessels) or **subepithelial** (below the skin surface lining) surfaces of the kidney's **glomerular basement membrane** (the bottom layer lining the glomerlus). Secondary glomerulonephritis occurs as a side-effect of chronic infectious, neoplastic, or immunologic disorders. Animals with **idiopathic** (where the cause is unknown) glomerulonephritis (>50% of cases) usually have signs of renal disease. Immune-Complex Glomerulonephritis affects many breeds.

Systemic Lupus Erythematosus. See above section on skin diseases.

Bowels

Inflammatory Bowel Disease ("Leaky Gut" Syndrome; IBD). A condition in which the stomach and/or intestine is chronically infiltrated by inflammatory cells. These cells include lymphocytes and plasma cells, which are directly responsible for the body's immune response. Eosinophils are another cell type commonly present here.

The causes of IBD include genetic predisposition, nutrition, infectious agents, and abnormalities of the immune system, including immune-mediated reactions to dietary proteins (food intolerance or hypersensitivity, especially to glutens).

IBD is common and affects many breeds.

Central nervous system

Immune-Complex Meningoencephalitis. A condition that is also called periarteritis nodosa in people. Steroid-responsive meningitis has been seen in adolescent or young adult dogs. The clinical signs consist of cyclic bouts of fever, severe neck pain and rigidity, reluctance to move, and depression. Each attack lasts five-to-10 days, with intervening periods of complete or partial normalcy lasting a week or more. During attacks, the cerebral spinal fluid contains increased amounts of protein and **neutrophils** (a type of white blood cell). The lesion is an **arteritis** (an inflammation of the walls of the arteries), primarily of the blood vessels of the lining of the **meninges** (brain), but it occasionally affects other organs as well.

The disease is often self-limiting over several months, and attacks become milder and less frequent. In some animals, the disease becomes chronic and only partially amenable to immunosuppressive therapy.

The predisposed breeds include: the Akita Inu; Beagle; Bernese Mountain Dog; Boxer; German Shorthaired Pointer; and Weimaraner.

Polyglandular Autoimmune Syndrome. The combination of autoimmune thyroiditis and other autoimmune diseases (as listed above) results in **Polyglandular Autoimmune Syndrome**, which occurs when multiple endocrine glands, and sometimes also non-endocrine systems, malfunction simultaneously. The symptoms of polyglandular autoimmune syndrome depend on the glands in question and the resulting hormonal deficiencies. This condition, which has long been identified in people, is becoming more commonly recognized in the dog, and probably also occurs in other species. It tends to run in families and is believed to be inherited.

The most commonly recognized polyglandular syndrome of dogs is **Schmidt's Syndrome** (a combination of autoimmune thyroiditis and **Addison's disease**). Addison's disease is an immune-mediated hypoadrenocorticism where the disease process progressively destroys the tissues of the adrenal glands, much like diabetes destroys the pancreas. This is a heritable trait which to date has been recognized in more than 20 dog breeds.

Case study

Mystic, a three-year-old, neutered male Nova Scotia Duck Tolling Retriever, was re-trieving in a duck blind when he suddenly collapsed and was very pale and lifeless. Attempts to revive him with honey met with partial success, and he was rushed to a nearby emergency clinic. Upon examination, he was diagnosed with **exertional physiological shock** (shock precipitated by physical exertion). The astute clinician on duty recognized the possibility of Addison's disease because of Mystic's breed and his clinical signs.

Sure enough, specialized diagnostic testing and an abdominal ultrasound confirmed the diagnosis (he had a very low non-responsive ACTH Stimulation Test, and very small adrenal glands). Mystic was started on therapy with monthly injections of Percorten®-V (Novartis) along with low daily doses of prednisone and table salt add-ed to his food.

Mystic improved dramatically for several months, then began to slide backwards with reduced energy, poor coat texture, and lack of focus during duck trials. His adrenal function was retested and was properly balanced on his combination therapy, but his cholesterol level was slightly elevated and he had borderline anemia. Further testing revealed autoimmune thyroiditis with elevated T3 autoantibodies and high thyro-globulin autoantibody. This possibility was pursued not only because of his new clini-cal signs and screening lab test results, but also because up to two-thirds of Addison's disease patients (human and animal) also have autoimmune thyroiditis.

Therapy with twice-daily thyroxine was added to Mystic's treatment and he responded immediately by returning to his former athletic self. His breeder was notified of his double autoimmune endocrine disease, and promised to follow up by testing all of Mystic's close relatives and parents.

Appendix B

Dosing Equivalents of Natural Thyroid Hormone Extracts* to Synthetic
Thyroxine Hormone Replacement

Natural Thyroid Extract	Synthetic Thyroxine	
1/4 grain	18.5 mcg	[0.012 mg]
1/2 grain	37 mcg	[0.035 mg]
1 grain	74 mcg	[0.075 mg]
1 1/2 grains	111 mcg	[0.10 mg]
2 grains	148 mcg	[0.15 mg]
3 grains	222 mcg	[0.20 mg]
4 grains	296 mcg	[0.30 mg]
5 grains	370 mcg	[0.35 mg]

*Armour Thyroid (Forest Labs), Naturethroid and Westhroid (RLC Labs), Thyroid®
(ERFA Canada)

APPENDIX C

HEMOPET / HEMOLIFE
11561 Salinaz Avenue
Garden Grove, California 92843
Phone 714-891-2022
Fax 714-891-2123
www.hemopet.org; hemopet@hotmail.com

THYROID GOLD™ REGISTRATION CERTIFICATE

This is to certify that _____, Reg. # _____,

owned by _____, has

successfully earned the THYROID GOLD™ Registration Certificate.

Testing was performed on, Date _____; Hemolife Acc. # _____.

Certificate Number: _____   _____
                                        W. Jean Dodds, DVM
                                        President

A sample Thyroid GOLD™ certificate from Hemopet/Hemolife for those dogs qualifying with a normal thyroid antibody profile.

ABOUT THE AUTHORS

Dr. W. Jean Dodds received the D.V.M. degree with honors in 1964 from the Ontario Veterinary College, University of Toronto. In 1965, she accepted a position with the New York State Health Department in Albany and began comparative studies of animals with inherited and acquired bleeding diseases. Her position there began as a Research Scientist and culminated as Chief, Laboratory of Hematology, Wadsworth Center.

In 1980, she also became Executive Director, New York State Council on Human Blood and

Author W. Jean Dodds, DVM with Issho.

Transfusion Services. This work continued full-time until 1986 when she moved to Southern California to establish Hemopet, the first nonprofit national blood bank program for animals.

From 1965-1986, she was a member of many national and international committees on hematology, animal models of human disease, veterinary medicine, and laboratory animal science. Dr. Dodds was a grantee of the National Heart, Lung, and Blood Institute (NIH) and has over 150 research publications.

She was formerly President of the Scientist's Center for Animal Welfare, Chairman of the Committee on Veterinary Medical Sciences, and Vice-Chairman of the Institute of Laboratory Animal Resources, National Academy of Sciences. In 1974, Dr. Dodds was selected as Outstanding Woman Veterinarian of the Year, AVMA Annual Meeting, Denver, Colorado; in 1977 received the Region I Award for Outstanding Service to the Veterinary Profession from the American Animal Hospital Association, Cherry Hill, New Jersey; in 1978 and 1990 received the Gaines Fido Award as Dogdom's Woman of the Year; and the Award of Merit in 1978 in Recognition of Special Contributions to the Veterinary Profession from the American Animal Hospital Association, Salt Lake City, Utah.

In 1984, she was awarded the Centennial Medal from the University of Pennsylvania School of Veterinary Medicine. She was elected a distinguished Practitioner of the National Academy of Practice in Veterinary Medicine in 1987. In 1994, she was given the Holistic Veterinarian of the Year Award from the American Holistic Veterinary Medical Association. She was the Editor of *Advances in Veterinary Science and Comparative Medicine* for Academic Press, and is an active member of numerous professional societies. She was recently a member of the National Research Council/BANR Committee on National Needs for Research in Veterinary Science, which released its report in July 2005. She is an inventor and holds numerous patents. She and her husband, Charles Berman, a patent attorney, live in Santa Monica, California.

Hemopet commenced operations in 1986 and its range of nonprofit services and educational activities include:

- Providing canine blood components, blood bank supplies, and related services.

- Adopting retired Greyhound blood donors as companions through Pet Life-Line.

- Contributing to the social needs of the less fortunate in our society by volunteer and interactive programs with the Greyhounds.

- Consulting in clinical pathology through Hemopet/Hemolife, teaching animal health care professionals, companion animal fanciers, and pet owners on hematology and blood banking, immunology, endocrinology, nutrition and holistic medicine, nationwide and overseas.

Diana R. Laverdure

Diana R. Laverdure received a bachelor of arts degree in English *magna cum laude* in 1987 from Tufts University. A lifelong dog lover and professional writer for more than 20 years, she has combined her two passions as a frequent contributing writer on dog health and dog care topics to a variety of national publications. Her 2009 article, "Hold that Needle" for the *Natural Dog* annual (Bow Tie) on the dangers of canine over-vaccination, earned

Author Diana Laverdure with Chase.

her a nomination for best feature in a yearbook, annual, or special edition magazine from the Dog Writers Association of America (DWAA). She is also the creator of the award-winning Web site, The Happy Dog Spot (http://www.the-happy-dog-spot.com), which provides dog enthusiasts with trusted information to help them raise healthy, happy canine companions.

Diana's awareness of the heart-wrenching plight of homeless animals was heightened in January 2002, when she adopted the four-legged love of her life, Chase, from the Tri County Humane Society, a no-kill animal shelter located in Boca Raton, Florida. Since that time, she has provided the shelter with ongoing media publicity services *pro bono,* which has resulted in increased awareness for the organization and its life-saving work within Palm Beach, Broward, and Miami-Dade counties. She also serves on the shelter's board of directors, participating in shaping its future growth and direction. She and Chase reside in Boynton Beach, Florida.

References

Chapter 1

Berry, M.J., & Larsen, P.R. "The role of selenium in thyroid hormone action." *Endocrine Reviews*, 13(2): 207-221 (1992).

Braverman, L. E., & Utiger, R. D. *The thyroid: A fundamental and clinical text*. Philadelphia, PA: Lippincott Williams and Wilkins, 2000.

de los Santos, E. T., Keyhani-Rofagha, S., Cunningham, J. J., & Mazzaferri, E. L. "Cystic thyroid nodules: The dilemma of malignant lesions." *Annals of Internal Medicine*, 150:1422-1427 (1990).

Diaz Espineira, M. M., Mol, J.A., Peeters, M. E., Pollak, Y.W.E.A., et al. "Assessment of thyroid function in dogs with low plasma thyroxine concentration." *Journal of Veterinary Internal Medicine*. 21: 25–32 (2007).

Dalir-Naghadeh, B., & Rezaei, S. A. "Assessment of serum thyroid hormone concentrations in lambs with selenium deficiency myopathy." *American Journal of Veterinary Research*. 69: 659-663 (2008).

Dodds, W.J. "Autoimmune thyroid disease." *Dog World*. 77.4: 36-40 (1992).

Dodds, W. J. "Thyroid can alter behavior." *Dog World*. 77.10: 40-42 (1992).

Dodds, W. J. "Estimating disease prevalence with health surveys and genetic screening." *Advances Veterinary Science Comparative Medicine*. 39: 29-96 (1995).

Dodds, W. J. "Practical understanding of thyroid disease." *Proceedings of the American Holistic Veterinary Medical Association*. 2009: 71-78.

Falk, S.A., ed. *Thyroid disease: Endocrinology, surgery, nuclear medicine and radiotherapy (2nd ed.).* Philadelphia, PA, Lippincott-Raven, 1997.

Fisher, D. A. "Thyroid Disorders." *Principles and practice of medical genetics.* Rimoin, D. L., Connor, J.M., & Dyeritz, R. E., New York: Churchill Livingstone, 1997: 1365–1377.

Fisher, D. A., Pandian, M. R., & Carlton E. *Autoimmune thyroid disease: An expanding spectrum.* Pediatric Clinics of North America. 34: 907-918 (1987).

Fyfe, J. C., Kampschmidt, K., Dang, V., & Poteet, B. A., et al. "Congenital hypothyroidism with goiter in toy fox terriers." *Journal of Veterinary Internal Medicine.* 17: 50-57 (2003).

Happ, G.M. "Thyroiditis: A model canine autoimmune disease." *Advances Veterinary Science Comparative Medicine.* 39: 97-139 (1993).

Happ, G. M., Ollier, W., & Kennedy, L. J. "Genetic determinants of susceptibility to hypothyroid disease in dogs." AKC Research Foundation Report. International Symposium on Canine Hypothyroidism, University of California, Davis. Canine Practice. 2005: 4-62.

"International symposium on canine hypothyroidism." University of California, Davis. *Canine Practice.* 22(1): 4-62 (1997).

Kennedy, L. J., Quarmby, S., Happ, G. M., Barnes, A., et al. "Association of canine hypothyroid disease with a common major histocompatibility complex DLA class II allele." *Tissue Antigens.* 68: 82-86 (2006).

Kennedy, L. J., Hudson, H. J, Leonard, J., Angles, J. M., et al. "Association of hypothyroid disease in doberman pinscher dogs with a rare major histocompatibility complex DLA class II haplotype." *Tissue Antigens.* 67: 53-56 (2005).

Schmidt, M. A., & Bland, J. S. "Thyroid gland as sentinel: Interface between internal and external environment." *Alternative Therapies.* 3: 78-81 (1997).

Scott-Moncrieff JC. Hypothyroidism. In: Ettinger SJ, Feldman EC, eds. *Textbook of veterinary internal medicine.* 7th ed. St. Louis, Mo: Saunders Elsevier, 2010:1753.

Sinha, A. A., Lopez, M. T., & McDevitt, H. O. "Autoimmune diseases: The failure of self tolerance." *Science.* 248: 1380-1388 (1990).

Tizard, I. R., & Schubot, R. M. *Veterinary immunology: An introduction (6th ed.).* Philadelphia, PA: WB Saunders, 2000: 480.

Tomer, Y., & Davies, T. F. "Infection, thyroid disease, and autoimmunity." *Endocrine Reviews.* 14: 107-120 (1993).

Chapter 2

Bell, J. S. "Hereditary hypothyroidism: Understanding the disease process." *AKC Gazette.* 118(8): 24-27 (2001).

Berry, M. J., & Larsen, P. R. "The role of selenium in thyroid hormone action." *Endocrine Reviews.* 13(2): 207-219 (1992).

Buenevicius, R. "Role of thyroid hormones in mental disorders." *Current Opinion Psychiatry.* 22: 391-395 (2009).

Cerundolo, R., Court, M. H., & Hao, Q., et al. "Identification and concentration of soy phytoestrogens in commercial dog foods." *American Journal of Veterinary Research.* 65: 592-596 (2004).

Cohen, A. D., & Shoenfeld, Y. "Vaccine-induced autoimmunity." *Journal of Autoimmunity.* 9: 699-703 (1996).

Diaz Espineira, M.M., Mol, J. A., Peeters, M.E., Pollak Y.W.E.A., et al. "Assessment of thyroid function in dogs with low plasma thyroxine concentration." *Journal of Veterinary Internal Medicine.* 21: 25–32 (2007).

Dodds, W.J. "Unraveling the autoimmune mystery." *Dog World.* 77: 44-48 (1992).

Dodds, W.J., & Donoghue S. "Interactions of clinical nutrition with genetics." *The Waltham Book of Clinical Nutrition of the Dog and Cat.* Oxford, Pergamon Press Ltd., 1994:105-117.

Dodds, W.J. "Estimating disease prevalence with health surveys and genetic screening." *Advances Veterinary Science Comparative Medicine.* 39: 29-96 (1995).

Dodds, W.J. "Autoimmune thyroiditis and polyglandular autoimmunity of purebred dogs." *Canine Practice.* 22(1): 18-19 (1997).

Dodds, W. J. "What's new in thyroid disease?" *Proceedings of the American Holistic Veterinary Medical Association.* 1997: 82-95.

Dodds, W. J. "Canine autoimmune thyroiditis: 1000 cases." *Proeedings of the American Holistic Veterinary Medical Association.* 1999: 77-79.

Dodds, W. J. "Complementary and alternative veterinary medicine: The immune system." *Clinical Techniques in Small Animal Practice.* 17: 58-63 (2002).

Dodds, W. J. "Practical understanding of thyroid disease." *Proceedings of the American Holistic Veterinary Medical Association.* 2009: 71-78.

Fein, H.G., & Rivlin, R.S. "Anemia in thyroid diseases." *Medical Clinics of North America.* 59: 1133-1145 (1975).

Fisher, D. A., Pandian, M. R., & Carlton, E. "Autoimmune thyroid disease: An expanding spectrum." *Pediatric Clinics of North America.* 34: 907-918 (1987).

Fort, P., Moses, N., Fasano, M., Goldberg, T., et al. "Breast and soy-formula feedings in early infancy and the prevalence of autoimmune thyroid disease in children." *Journal of the American College of Nutrition.* 9(2): 164-167 (1990).

Fyfe, J. C., Kampschmidt, K., Dang, V., Poteet, B. A., et al. "Congenital hypothyroidism with goiter in toy fox terriers." *Journal of Veterinary Internal Medicine.* 17: 50-57 (2003).

Greco, D. S., Feldman, E. C., Peterson, M. E., Turner, J. L., et al. "Congenital hypothyroid dwarfism in a family of giant schnauzers." *Journal of Veterinary Internal Medicine.* 5: 57-65 (1991).

Gupta, A., Eggo, M. C., Uetrecht, J. P., Cribb, A.E., et al. "Drug-induced hypothyroidism: The thyroid as a target organ in hypersensitivity reactions to anticonvulsants and sulfonamides." *Clinical Pharmacology and Therapeutics.* 51: 56-67 (1992).

Happ G.M. "Thyroiditis: A model canine autoimmune disease." *Advances Veterinary Science Comparative Medicine.* 39: 97-139 (1995).

Happ, G. M., Ollier, W., & Kennedy, L.J. "Genetic determinants of susceptibility to hypothyroid disease in dogs." *AKC Research Foundation Report.* 2005.

Horton, L., Coburn, R. J., England, J. M., & Himsworth, R. L. "The haematology of hypothyroidism." *Quarterly Journal of Medicine.* 45: 101-123 (1976).

"International symposium on canine hypothyroidism." University of California, Davis. *Canine Practice.* 22(1): 4-62 (1997).

Jaggy, A., Oliver, J. E., Ferguson, D. C., et al. "Neurological manifestations of hypothyroidism: A retrospective study of 29 dogs." *Journal of Veterinary Internal Medicine.* 8: 328-336 (1994).

Kaptein, E.M. "Thyroid hormone metabolism and thyroid diseases in chronic renal failure." *Endocrine Reviews.* 17: 45-63 (1996).

Kaswan, R. L., Martin, C. L, Dawe, D. L. "Keratoconjunctivitis sicca: Immunological evaluation of 62 canine cases. *American Journal of Veterinary Research.* 46: 376–383 (1985).

Kaswan, R. L., Bounous, D., & Hirsh, S. G. "Diagnosis and management of keratoconjunctivitis sicca." *Veterinary Medicine.* 90: 539-560 (1995).

Kennedy, L. J., Quarmby, S., Happ, G. M., Barnes, A., et al. "Association of canine hypothyroid disease with a common major histocompatibility complex DLA class II allele." *Tissue Antigens.* 68: 82-86 (2006).

Kennedy, L. J., Hudson, H. J., Leonard, J., Angles, J. M., et al. "Association of hypothyroid disease in Doberman pinscher dogs with a rare major histocompatibility complex DLA class II haplotype. " *Tissue Antigens.* 67: 53-56 (2005).

McGregor, A. M. "Autoimmunity in the thyroid: Can the molecular revolution contribute to our understanding?" *Quarterly Journal of Medicine.* 82: 1-13 (1992).

Panciera, D. L., & Johnson, G. S. "Hypothyroidism and von willebrand factor." *Journal of American Veterinary Medical Association.* 206: 595-596 (1995).

Panciera, D. L. "Clinical manifestations of canine hypothyroidism." *Veterinary Medicine.* 92: 44-49 (1997).

Panciera, D. L. "Hypothyroidism in dogs: 66 cases (1987-1992)." *Journal of American Veterinary Medical Association.* 204: 761-767 (1994).

Panciera, D. L., Purswell, B. J., & Kolster, K. A. "Effect of short-term hypothyroidism on reproduction in the bitch." *Theriogenology.* 68: 316-321 (2007).

Patterson, D. F. "Companion animal medicine in the age of medical genetics." *Journal of Veterinary Internal Medicine.* 14: 1-9 (2000).

Peruccio, C. "Incidence of hypothyroidism in dogs affected by keratoconjuctivitis sicca." *Transactions American College of Veterinary Ophthalmology.* 47-48 (1982).

Plummer, C.E., Specht, A., & Gelatt, K. N. "Ocular manifestations of endocrine disease." *Compendium on Continuing Education for the Practicing Veterinarian.* 12: 733-743 (2007).

Rose, N. R., Rasooly, L., Saboori, A.M., & Burek, C. L. "Linking iodine with autoimmune thyroiditis." *Environmental Health Perspectives.* 107 suppl 5: 749-752 (1999).

Rugg, L. C. "Coping with thyroid disease." *AKC Gazette.* 120(7): 48-51 (2003).

Schmidt, M. A, & Bland, J.S. "Thyroid gland as sentinel: Interface between internal and external environment." *Alternative Therapies.* 3: 78-81 (1997).

Scott-Moncrieff JC. "Hypothyroidism." In: Ettinger SJ, Feldman EC, eds. *Textbook of veterinary internal medicine.* 7th ed. St. Louis, Mo: Saunders Elsevier, 2010:1753.

Surks, M. I., & Sievert, R. "Drugs and thyroid function." *New England Journal of Medicine.* 333: 1688-1694 (1995).

Tomer, Y., & Davies, T. F. "Infection, thyroid disease, and autoimmunity." *Endocrine Reviews.* 14: 107-120 (1993).

Vajner, L. "Lymphocytic thyroiditis in beagle dogs in a breeding colony: Findings of serum autoantibodies." *Veterinary Medicine Czech.* 11: 333-338 (1997).

White, H. L., Freeman, L. M., Mahony, O., et al. "Effect of dietary soy on serum thyroid hormone concentrations in healthy adult cats." *American Journal of Veterinary Research.* 65: 586-591 (2004).

Chapter 3

Aronson, L. P., & Dodds, W. J. "The effect of hypothyroid function on canine behavior." *Proceedings of International Veterinary Behavior Medicine.* 2005.

Aronson, L. P., & Dodman, N. H. "Thyroid function as a cause of aggression in dogs and cats." *Proceedings of Deutsche Veterinaermedizinsche Gesellschaft.* 1997: 228.

Beaver, B. V., Haug, L. I. "Canine behaviors associated with hypothyroidism." *Journal of American Animal Hospital Association.* 39: 431-434 (2003).

Buenevicius, R. "Role of thyroid hormones in mental disorders." *Current Opinion Psychiatry.* 22: 391-395 (2009).

Cameron, D. L., & Crocker, A. D. "The hypothyroid rat as a model of increased sensitivity to dopamine receptor agonists." *Pharmacology Biochemistry and Behavior.* 37: 627-632 (1995).

Carter, G. R., Scott-Moncrieff, J. C., Leuscher AU, & Moore G. "Serum total thyroxine and thyroid stimulating hormone concentrations in dogs with behavior problems." *Journal of Veterinary Behavior.* 4: 230-236 (2009).

Cauzinille, L. "Neurological consequences of thyroid disorders." *Proceedings of the World Small Animal Veterinary Assocation.* 2005.

Cox, D. "Is Fido acting strange? It could be his thyroid." *Animal Wellness.* 6(2): 14-15 (2005).

de los Santos, E. T., Keyhani-Rofagha, S., Cunningham, J. J., & Mazzaferri, E. L. "Cystic thyroid nodules: The dilemma of malignant lesions." *Annals of Internal Medicine.* 150: 1422-1427 (1990).

Denicoff, K. D., Joffe, R. T., Lakschmanan, M.C., Robbins, J., & Rubinow, D. R. "Neuropsychiatric manifestations of altered thyroid state." *American Journal of Psychiatry.* 147: 94-99 (1990).

Dewey, C. W., Shelton, G. D., & Bailey, C.S. "Neuromuscular dysfunction in five dogs with acquired myasthenia gravis and presumptive hypothyroidism." *Progressive Veterinary Neurology.* 6: 117-123 (1995).

Dodds ,W. J. "Thyroid can alter behavior." *Dog World.* 77(10): 40-42 (1992).

Dodds ,W. J. "Apply systemic diagnostic plan to assess aggression: Behavior linked to thyroid disease." *DVM Magazine.* 23(5): 22–23 (1992).

Dodds, W.J. "Behavioral changes associated with thyroid dysfunction in dogs." *Proceedings of the American Holistic Veterinary Medical Association*. 1999: 80-82.

Dodds, W. J. "Behavioral issues with thyroiditis: Theory and case review." *Proceedings of the American Holistic Veterinary Medical Association*. 2004: 55-59.

Dodman, N. H., Mertens, P. A., & Aronson, L. P. "Aggression in two hypothyroid dogs, behavior case of the month." *Journal of American Veterinary Medical Association*. 207: 1168-1171 (1992).

Hauser, P., Zametkin, A. J., Martinez, P., et al. "Attention deficit-hyperactivity disorder in people with generalized resistance to thyroid hormone." *New England Journal of Medicine*. 328: 997-1001 (1993).

Henley, W. N., Chen, X., Klettner, C., Bellush, L. L., & Notestine, M. A. "Hypothyroidism increases serotonin turnover and sympathetic activity in the adult rat." *Canadian Journal of Physiology and Pharmacology*. 69: 205-210 (1991).

Overall, K. L. *Clinical Behavioral Medicine for the Small Animal*. St. Louis, Mosby, 1998.

Uchida, Y., Dodman, N. H., DeNapoli, J., & Aronson, L. P. "Characterization and treatment of 20 canine dominance aggression cases." *Journal of Veterinary Medical Sciences*. 59: 397-399 (1997).

Wicklund, B. "Gland illusion." *ACK Gazette*. 127(3): 36-39 (2010).

Chapter 4
Antech News. "Laboratory data in geriatric dogs and cats." April 2001.

Dodds, W. J. "What's new in thyroid disease?" *Proceedings of the American Holistic Veterinary Medical Association*. 1997: 82-95.

Dodds, W. J. "Canine autoimmune thyroiditis:1000 cases." *Proceedings of the American Holistic Veterinary Medical Association*. 1999: 77-79.

Dodds, W. J. "Practical understanding of thyroid disease." *Proceedings of the American Holistic Veterinary Medical Association*. 2009: 71-78.

Fyfe, J. C., Kampschmidt, K., Dang, V., Poteet, B. A., et al "Congenital hypothyroidism with goiter in toy fox terriers." *Journal of Veterinary Internal Medicine*. 17: 50-57 (2003).

Greco, D. S., Feldman, E. C., Peterson, M. E., Turner, J. L., et al. "Congenital hypothyroid dwarfism in a family of giant schnauzers." *Journal of Veterinary Internal Medicine*. 5: 57-65 (1999).

Kaswan, R. L., Martin, C. L., Dawe, & D. L. "Keratoconjunctivitis sicca: Immunological evaluation of 62 canine cases." *American Journal of Veterinary Research*. 46: 4376–383 (1985).

Kaswan, R. L., Bounous, & D., Hirsh, S. G. "Diagnosis and management of keratoconjunctivitis sicca." *Veterinary Medicine*. 90: 539-560 (1995).

Klaus, G., Giuliano, E. A., Moore, C. P., Stuhr, C. M., et al. "Keratoconjunctivitis sicca associated with administration of etodolac in dogs: 21 cases (1992-2002)." *Journal of American Veterinary Medical Association*. 230: 541-547 (2007).

Panciera, D. L. "Clinical manifestations of canine hypothyroidism." *Veterinary Medicine*. 92: 44-49 (1997).

Panciera, D. L. "Hypothyroidism in dogs: 66 cases (1987-1992)." *Journal of American Veterinary Medical Association*. 204: 761-767 (1994).

Panciera, D. L, Purswell, B. J., & Kolster, K. A. "Effect of short-term hypothyroidism on reproduction in the bitch." *Theriogenology*. 68: 316-321 (2007).

Chapter 5—Drugs

Brenner, K., Harkin, K., Schermerhorn, T. "Iatrogenic, sulfonamide-induced hypothyroid crisis in a Labrador retriever." *Australian Veterinary Journal*. 87: 503-505 (2009).

Gupta, A., Eggo, M. C., Uetrecht, J. P., Cribb, A. E., et al. "Drug-induced hypothyroidism: the thyroid as a target organ in hypersensitivity reactions to anticonvulsants and sulfonamides." *Clinical Pharmacology and Therapeutics*. 51: 56-67 (1992).

Hall, I. A., Campbell, K. C., Chambers, M. D., et al. "Effect of trimethoprim-sulfamethoxazole on thyroid function in dogs with pyoderma." *Journal of the American Veterinary Medical Association*. 202: 1959-1962 (1993).

Klaus, G., Giuliano, E. A., Moore, C. P., Stuhr, C. M. et al. "Keratoconjunctivitis sicca associated with administration of etodolac in dogs: 21 cases (1992-2002)." *Journal of the American Veterinary Medical Association*. 230: 541-547 (2007).

Seelig, D. M., Whittemore, J. C., Lappin, M. R., Myers, A. M. et al. "Goitrous hypothyroidism associated with treatment with trimethoprim-sulfamethoxazole in a young dog." *Journal of the American Veterinary Medical Association*. 232: 1181-1185 (2008).

Surks, M, I., & Sievert, R. "Drugs and thyroid function." *New England Journal of Medicine*. 333: 1688-1694 (1995).

Chapter 5—General

Dewey, C.W., Shelton, G.D., & Bailey, C. S. "Neuromuscular dysfunction in five dogs with acquired myasthenia gravis and presumptive hypothyroidism." *Progress in Veterinary Neurology*. 6: 117-123 (1995).

Plummer, C. E., Specht, A., & Gelatt, K. N. "Ocular manifestations of endocrine disease." *Compendium on Continuing Education for the Practicing Veterinarian.* 12: 733-743 (2007).

Schmidt, M.A., & Bland, J. S. "Thyroid gland as sentinel: Interface between internal and external environment." *Alternative Therapies.* 3: 78-81 (1997).

Chapter 5—Nutrition

Bauer, J.E. "Evaluation of nutraceuticals, dietary supplements, and functional food ingredients for companion animals." *Journal of American Veterinary Medical Association.* 218: 1755-1760 (2001).

Berry, M.J., & Larsen, P.R. "The role of selenium in thyroid hormone action." *Endocrine Reviews.* 13(2): 207-219 (1992).

Burkholder, W.J., & Swecker, W.S. Jr. "Nutritional influences on immunity." *Seminars in Veterinary Medicine and Surgery (Small Animals).* 5(3): 154-156 (1990).

Castillo, V.A., Rodriguez, M. S., Lalia, J. C., & Pisarev, M. A. "Morphologic changes in the thyroid glands of puppies fed a high-iodine commercial diet." *International Journal of Applied Research in Veterinary Medicine.* 1(1): 1-8 (2003).

Cerundolo, R., Court, M. H., Hao, Q. et al. "Identification and concentration of soy phytoestrogens in commercial dog foods." *American Journal of Veterinary Research.* 65: 592-596 (2003).

Cousins, R. J. "Nutritional regulation of gene expression." *American Journal of Medicine,* 106: 20S-23S (1999).

Dalir-Naghadeh, B., & Rezaei, S. A. "Assessment of serum thyroid hormone concentrations in lambs with selenium deficiency myopathy." *American Journal of Veterinary Research.* 69: 659-663 (2008).

Daniel, H. "Genomics and proteomics: Importance for the future of nutrition research." *British Journal of Nutrition.* 87: S305-S311 (2002).

Dereszynski, D.M., Center SA, Randolph JF, Brooks MB et al. "Clinical and clinico-pathologic features of dogs that consumed foodborne hepatotoxic aflatoxins: 72 cases (2005–2006)." *Journal of American Veterinary Medical Association.* 232: 1329-1337 (2008).

der Marderosian, Q. A. *The Review of Natural Products: Facts and Comparisons.* St. Louis, MO: Lippincott, Williams & Wilkins, 2001: 389-390, 508-509.

Dodds, W. J., & Donoghue, S. "Interactions of clinical nutrition with genetics." in: *The Waltham Book of Clinical Nutrition of the Dog and Cat.* Oxford: Pergamon Press Ltd., 1994:105-117.

Dodds, W. J. "Pet food preservatives and other additives. *Complementary and Alternative Veterinary Medicine*. St. Louis, Mosby, 1997: 73-79.

Elliott, R., & Ong, T. J. "Science, medicine, and the future: Nutritional genomics." *British Medical Journal*. 324: 1438-1442 (2002).

Fekete, S.G., & Brown, D. L. "Veterinary aspects and perspectives of nutrigenomics: A critical review." *Acta Veterinaria Hungarica*. 55(2): 229–239 (2007).

Fort, P., Moses, N., Fasano, M., Goldberg, T. et al. "Breast and soy-formula feedings in early infancy and the prevalence of autoimmune thyroid disease in children." *Journal of American College Nutrition*. 9(2): 164-167 (1990).

German, J. B., Roberts, M. A., Fay, L., & Watkins, S. M. "Metabolomics and individual metabolic assessment: The next great challenge for nutrition." *Journal of Nutrition*. 132: 2486-2487 (2002).

Müller, M., & Kersten, S. "Nutrogenetics: Goals and strategies." *Nature Reviews Genetics*. 4: 315 -322 (2003).

Rose, N. R., Rasooly, L., Saboori, A. M., & Burek, C. L. "Linking iodine with autoimmune thyroiditis." *Environmental Health Perspectives*. 107. suppl 5: 749-752 (1999).

Roudebush, P. "Ingredients associated with adverse food reactions in dogs and cats." *Advances Small Animal Medical and Surgery*. 15(9): 1-3 (2002).

Stogdale, L. "Information sources on canine and feline nutrition." *Canadian Veterinary Journal*. 45: 8 (2004).

Swanson, K. S., & Schook, L. B. "Canine nutritional model: Influence of age, diet, and genetics on health and well-being." *Current Nutrition and Food Science*. 2(2): 115-126 (2006).

Swanson, K. S., Schook, L. B., & Fahey, Jr G.C. "Nutritional genomics: Implications for companion animals." *Journal of Nutrition*. 133: 3033-3040 (2003).

Vojdani, A. "Detection of IgE, IgG, IgA and IgM antibodies against raw and processed food antigens." *Nutrition & Metabolism*. 6: 22-37 (2009).

White, H. L., Freeman, L. M., Mahony, O. et al. "Effect of dietary soy on serum thyroid hormone concentrations in healthy adult cats." *American Journal of Veterinary Research*. 65: 586-591 (2004).

Wynn, S. G., Bartges, J., & Dodds, W. J. "Raw meaty bones-based diets may cause prerenal azotemia in normal dogs." *AAVN Nutrition Research Symposium*. 2003.

Chapter 5—Pesticides
Anadon, A., Martinez-Larrañaga, & Martinez, M. A. "Use and abuse of pyrethrins and synthetic pyrethroids in veterinary medicine." *The Veterinary Journal.* 182: 7-20 (2009).

Draper, M. "An open letter from Hartz to the Center for Public Integrity." 2009.

Glickman, L. T., Schofer, F. S., McKee, L. J., et al. "Epidemiologic study of insecticide exposures, obesity, and risk of bladder cancer in household dogs." *Journal of Toxicology Environmental Health.* 28: 407–414 (1989).

Glickman, L. T., Raghavan, M., Knapp, D. W., et al. "Herbicide exposure and the risk of transitional cell carcinoma of the urinary bladder in scottish terriers." *Journal of the American Veterinary Medical Association.* 224: 1290–1297 (2004).

Pell, M. B., & Olsen, J. "Pets and pesticides: Let's be careful out there." *The Center for Public Integrity.* 2008.

Chapter 5—Vaccines
Carmichael, L. E. "Canine viral vaccines at a turning point: A personal perspective." *Advances Veterinary Medicine.* 41: 289-307 (1999).

Carmichael, L. E. "An annotated historical account of canine parvovirus." *Journal of Veterinary Medicine, Series B.* 52: 303-311 (2005).

Cohen, A. D, & Shoenfeld, Y. "Vaccine-induced autoimmunity." *Journal of Autoimmunity.* 9: 699-703 (1996).

Dodds, W. J. "Immune-mediated diseases of the blood." *Advances Veterinary Science Comparative Medicine.* 27: 163-196 (1983).

Dodds, W. J. "Estimating disease prevalence with health surveys and genetic screening." *Advances Veterinary Science Comparative Medicine.* 39: 29-96 (1995).

Dodds, W. J. "Vaccine-related issues." *Complementary and Alternative Veterinary Medicine.* St. Louis, Mosby, 1997: 701-712.

Dodds, W. J. "More bumps on the vaccine road." *Advances Veterinary Medicine.* 41: 715-732 (1999).

Dodds, W. J. "Vaccination protocols for dogs predisposed to vaccine reactions." *Journal of the American Animal Hospital Association.* 38: 1-4 (2009).

Dodds, W. J. "Complementary and alternative veterinary medicine: the immune system." *Clinical Techniques in Small Animal Practice.* 17: 58-63 (2002).

Dodds WJ. "Vaccine issues revisited: What's really happening?" *Proceedings of the American Holistic Veterinary Medical Association.* 2007: 132-140.

Duval, D., & Giger, U. "Vaccine-associated immune-mediated hemolytic anemia in the dog." *Journal of Veterinary Internal Medicine*. 10: 290-295 (1996).

Hogenesch, H., Azcona-Olivera, J., Scott-Moncreiff, C., et al. "Vaccine-induced autoimmunity in the dog." *Advances Veterinary Medicine*. 41: 733-744 (1999).

Hustead, D.R., Carpenter, T., Sawyer, D. C., et al. "Vaccination issues of concern to practitioners." *Journal of American Veterinary Medical Association*. 214: 1000-1002 (1999).

Kyle, A. H. M., Squires, R. A., & Davies, P. R. "Serologic status and response to vaccination against canine distemper (CDV) and canine parvovirus (CPV) of dogs vaccinated at different intervals." *Journal of Small Animal Practice*. June, 2002.

Lappin, M. R., Andrews, J., Simpson, D., et al. "Use of serologic tests to predict resistance to feline herpesvirus 1, feline calicivirus, and feline parvovirus infection in cats." *Journal of American Veterinary Medical Association*. 220: 38-42 (2002).

Larson, L. J., & Schultz, R. D. "Effect of vaccination with recombinant canine distemper virus vaccine immediately before exposure under shelter-like conditions." *Veterinary Therapeutics*. 7: 113-118 (2006).

Larson, L. J., & Schultz, R. D. "Do two current canine parvovirus type 2 and 2b vaccines provide protection against the new type 2-c variant?" *Veterinary Therapeutics*. 9: 94-101 (2008).

McGaw, D. L., Thompson, M., Tate, D., et al. "Serum distemper virus and parvovirus antibody titers among dogs brought to a veterinary hospital for revaccination." *Journal of American Veterinary Medical Association*. 213: 72-75 (1998).

Moore, G. E., & Glickman, L. T. "A perspective on vaccine guidelines and titer tests for dogs." *Journal of American Veterinary Medical Association*. 224: 200-203 (2004).

Moore, G. E., Guptill, L. F., Ward, M. P., Glickman, N. W., et al. "Adverse events diagnosed within three days of vaccine administration in dogs." *Journal of the American Veterinary Medical Association*. 227: 1102–1108 (2005).

Mouzin, D. E., Lorenzen, M. J., Haworth, et al. "Duration of serologic response to five viral antigens in dogs." *Journal of American Veterinary Medical Association*. 224: 55-60 (2004).

Mouzin, D. E., Lorenzen, M. J., Haworth, et al. "Duration of serologic response to three viral antigens in cats." *Journal of American Veterinary Medical Association*. 224: 61-66 (2004).

Paul, M. A. "Credibility in the face of controversy." *American Animal Hospital Association Trends Magazine*. XIV(2): 19-21 (1998).

Paul, M. A. et al. "Report of the AAHA Canine Vaccine Task Force: 2003 canine vaccine guidelines, recommendations, and supporting literature." *Journal of American Animal Hospital Association.* April, 2003: 28pp.

Paul, M. A., et al. "Report of the AAHA canine vaccine task force: 2006 AAHA canine vaccine guidelines." *Journal of American Animal Hospital Association.* 42: 80-109 (2006). www.aahanet.org.

Phillips, T. R., Jenson, J. L., Rubino, M., et al. "Effects of vaccines on the canine system." *Canadian Journal of Veterinary Research.* 53:154-160 (1989).

Richards, J.R., Elston, T.H., Ford, R.B., et al. "The 2006 American Association of Feline Practitioner's Feline Vaccine Advisory Panel Report." *Journal of American Veterinary Medical Association.* 229: 1405-1144 (2006). www.aafponline.org.

Schultz, R. D. "Current and future canine and feline vaccination programs." *Veterinary Medicine.* 93: 233-254 (1998).

Schultz, R. D, Conklin, S. "The immune system and vaccines." *Compendium on Continuing Education for the Practicing Veterinarian.* 20: 5-18 (1998).

Schultz, R. D. "Considerations in designing effective and safe vaccination programs for dogs." In: Carmichael LE (editor), "Recent Advances in Canine Infectious Diseases." *International Veterinary Information Service.* 2000. www.ivis.org.

Schultz, R. D, Ford, R. B, & Olsen, J., Scott, F. "Titer testing and vaccination: A new look at traditional practices." *Veterinary Medicine.* 97: 1-13 (2002).

Scott, F. W., & Geissinger, C. M. "Long-term immunity in cats vaccinated with an inactivated trivalent vaccine." *American Journal of Veterinary Research.* 60: 652-658 (1999).

Scott-Moncrieff, J. C., Azcona-Olivera, J., Glickman, N. W., et al. "Evaluation of antithyroglobulin antibodies after routine vaccination in pet and research dogs." *Journal of American Veterinary Medical Association.* 221: 515-521 (2002).

Smith, C. A. "Are we vaccinating too much?" *Journal of American Veterinary Medical Association.* 207: 421-425 (1995).

Souayah, N., et al. "Small fiber neuropathy following vaccination for rabies, varicella, or Lyme disease." *Vaccine.* 10: 1016-1120 (2009).

Tizard, I. "Risks associated with use of live vaccines." *Journal of American Veterinary Medical Association.* 196: 1851-1858 (1990).

Tizard, I., & Ni, Y. "Use of serologic testing to assess immune status of companion animals." *Journal of American Veterinary Medical Association.* 213: 54-60 (1998).

Twark, L., & Dodds, W. J. "Clinical application of serum parvovirus and distemper virus antibody titers for determining revaccination strategies in healthy dogs." *Journal of American Veterinary Medical Association.* 217: 1021-1024 (2000).

Vascellari, M., Melchiotti, E., Bozza, M. A., et al. "Fibrosarcomas at presumed sites of injection in dogs: Characteristics and comparison with non-vaccination site fibrosarcomas and feline post-vaccinal fibrosarcomas." *Journal of Veterinary Medicine.* 50(6): 286-291 (2003).

Wilcock, B. P., & Yager, J. A. "Focal cutaneous vasculitis and alopecia at sites of rabies vaccination in dogs." *Journal of American Veterinary Medical Association.* 188: 1174-1177 (1986).

Chapter 6

Diaz Espineira, M. M., Mol, J. A., Peeters, M. E., Pollak, Y. W. E. A., Iversen, L.,van Dijk, J. E., Rijnberk, A., & Kooistra, H. S. "Assessment of thyroid function in dogs with low plasma thyroxine concentration." *Journal of Veterinary Internal Medicine.* 21: 25–32 (2007).

Dixon, R. M., Graham, P. A., & Mooney, C. T. "Serum thyrotropin concentrations: a new diagnostic test for canine hypothyroidism." *The Veterinary Record.* 138:594-595 (1996).

Ferm, K., Björnerfeldt, S., Karlsson, A., Andersson, G., et al. "Prevalence of diagnostic characteristics indicating canine autoimmune lymphocytic thyroiditis in giant schnauzer and hovawart dogs." *Journal of Small Animal Practice.* 50: 176-179 (2009).

Frank, L. A. "Comparison of thyrotropin-releasing hormone (TRH) to thyrotropin (TSH) stimulation for evaluating thyroid function in dogs." *Journal of the American Animal Hospital Association.* 32: 481-487 (1996).

Iverson, L., Jensen, A. L., Høier, R., et al. "Biological variation of canine serum thyrotropin (TSH) concentration." *Veterinary Clinical Pathology.* 28: 16-19 (1999).

Jensen, A. L., Iversen, L., Høier, R., et al. "Evaluation of an immunoradiometric assay for thyrotropin in serum and plasma samples of dogs with primary hypothyroidism." *Journal of Comparative Pathology.* 114: 339-346 (1996).

Lee, J. Y., Uzuka, Y., Tanabe, S., & Sarashina, T. "Prevalence of thyroglobulin "Prevalence of thyroglobulin autoantibodies detected by enzyme-linked immunosorbent assay of canine serum in hypothyroid, obese and healthy dogs in Japan." *Research in Veterinary Science.* 76: 129-132 (2004).

Nachreiner, R. F., & Refsal, K. R. "Radioimmunoassay monitoring of thyroid hormone concentrations in dogs on thyroid replacement therapy: 2,674 cases (1985-1987)." *Journal of American Veterinary Medical Association.* 201: 623-629 (1992).

Nachreiner, R. F., Refsal, K.R., Graham, P. A., et al. "Prevalence of autoantibodies to thyroglobulin in dogs with nonthyroidal illness." *American Journal of Veterinary Research*. 59: 951-955 (1998).

Nachreiner, R. F., Refsal, K. R., Graham, P. A., & Bowman, M. M. "Prevalence of serum thyroid hormone autoantibodies in dogs with clinical signs of hypothyroidism." *Journal of American Veterinary Medical Association*. 220: 466-471 (2002).

Panciera, D. L. "Thyroid-function testing: Is the future here?" *Veterinary Medicine*. 92: 50-57 (1997).

Paradis, M., Pagé, N., Larivière, N., et al. "Serum-free thyroxine concentrations, measured by chemiluminescence assay before and after thyrotropin administration in healthy dogs, hypothyroid dogs, and euthyroid dogs with dermatopathies." *Canadian Veterinary Journal*. 37: 289-294 (1996).

Peterson, M. E., Melian, C., & Nichols, R. "Measurement of serum total thyroxine, triiodothyronine, free thyroxine, and thyrotropin concentrations for diagnosis of hypothyroidism in dogs." *Journal of American Veterinary Medical Association*. 211: 1396-1402 (1997).

Scott-Moncrieff, J. C. R., & Nelson, R. W. "Change in serum thyroid stimulating hormone concentration in response to administration of thyrotropin-releasing hormone to healthy dogs, hypothyroid dogs, and euthyroid dogs with concurrent disease." *Journal of American Veterinary Medical Association*. 213: 1435-1438 (1998).

Scott-Moncrieff, J. C. R., Nelson, R. W., Bruner, J. M., et al. "Comparison of thyroid-stimulating hormone in healthy dogs, hypothyroid dogs, and euthyroid dogs with concurrent disease." *Journal of American Veterinary Medical Association*. 212: 387-391 (1998).

Scott-Moncrieff JC. "Hypothyroidism." In: Ettinger SJ, Feldman EC, eds. *Textbook of veterinary internal medicine*. 7th ed. St. Louis, Mo: Saunders Elsevier, 2010:1753.

Shiel RE, Brennan SF, Omodo-Eluk AJ, et al. "Thyroid hormone concentrations in young, healthy, pretraining greyhounds." *Veterinary Record* 161:616-619 (2007).

Shiel, R.E., Sist, M.D., Nachreiner, R.F., Ehrlich, C.P., et al. "Assessment of criteria used by veterinary practitioners to diagnose hypothyroidism in sighthounds and investigation of serum thyroid hormone concentrations in healthy Salukis." *Journal of American Veterinary Medical Association*. 236:302-308 (2010).

Thacker, E. L., Refsal, K. R., & Bull, R. W. "Prevalence of autoantibodies to thyroglobulin, thyroxine, or triiodothyronine and relationship of autoantibodies and serum concentration of iodothyronines in dogs." *American Journal of Veterinary Research*. 53: 449-453 (1992).

Thacker, E. L., Davis, J. M., Refsal, K. R., et al. "Isolation of thyroid peroxidase and lack of antibodies to the enzyme in dogs with autoimmune thyroid disease." *American Journal of Veterinary Research.* 56: 34-38 (1995).

Williams, D. A., Scott-Moncrieff, J.C., Bruner, J.M., et al. "Validation of an immunoassay for canine thyroid-stimulating hormone and changes in serum concentration following induction of h hypothyroidism in dogs." *Journal of the American Veterinary Medical Association.* 209: 1730-1732 (1996).

Chapter 7

Buenevicius, R., Kazanavicius, G., Zalinkevicius, R., et al. "Effects of thyroxine as compared with thyroxine plus triiodothyronine in patients with hypothyroidism." *New England Journal of Medicine.* 340: 424-429 (1999).

Graham, P. A., et al. "A 12-month prospective study of 234 thyroglobulin autoantibody positive dogs which had no laboratory evidence of thyroid dysfunction." *Proceedings 19th American College Veterinary Internal Medicine.* 2001: 105.

Nachreiner, R. F., & Refsal, K. R. "Radioimmunoassay monitoring of thyroid hormone concentrations in dogs on thyroid replacement therapy: 2,674 cases (1985-1987)." *Journal of American Veterinary Medical Association.* 201: 623-629 (1992).

Nachreiner, R. F., Refsal, K. R., Davis, W. R., et al. "Pharmacokinetics of l-thyroxine after its oral administration in dogs." *American Journal of Veterinary Research.* 54: 2091-2098 (1993).

Panciera, D. L. "Treating hypothyroidism." *Veterinary Medicine.* 92: 58-68 (1997).

Scott-Moncrieff JC. "Hypothyroidism." In: Ettinger SJ, Feldman EC, eds. *Textbook of veterinary internal medicine.* 7th ed. St. Louis, Mo: Saunders Elsevier, 2010:1753.

Shiel RE, Brennan SF, Omodo-Eluk AJ, et al. "Thyroid hormone concentrations in young, healthy, pretraining greyhounds." *Veterinary Record.* 161:616-619 (2007).

Shiel, R.E., Sist, M.D., Nachreiner, R.F., Ehrlich, C.P., et al. "Assessment of criteria used by veterinary practitioners to diagnose hypothyroidism in sighthounds and investigation of serum thyroid hormone concentrations in healthy Salukis." *Journal of American Veterinary Medical Association.* 236:302-308 (2010).

Volhard, W., & Brown, K. L. *The Holistic Guide for a Healthy Dog.* New York, Howell Book House, 1995.

INDEX

Entries designated with a p refer to photos between pages 88 and 89

From Dogwise Publishing
www.dogwise.com   1-800-776-2665

BEHAVIOR & TRAINING

ABC's of Behavior Shaping. Proactive Behavior Mgmt, DVD set. Ted Turner

Aggression In Dogs. Practical Mgmt, Prevention, & Behaviour Modification. Brenda Aloff

Am I Safe? DVD. Sarah Kalnajs

Barking. The Sound of a Language. Turid Rugaas

Behavior Problems in Dogs, 3rd ed. William Campbell

Brenda Aloff's Fundamentals: Foundation Training for Every Dog, DVD. Brenda Aloff

Bringing Light to Shadow. A Dog Trainer's Diary. Pam Dennison

Canine Behavior. A Photo Illustrated Handbook. Barbara Handelman

Canine Body Language. A Photographic Guide to the Native Language of Dogs. Brenda Aloff

Changing People Changing Dogs. Positive Solutions for Difficult Dogs. Rev. Dee Ganley

Chill Out Fido! How to Calm Your Dog. Nan Arthur

Clicked Retriever. Lana Mitchell

Do Over Dogs. Give Your Dog a Second Chance for a First Class Life. Pat Miller

Dog Behavior Problems. The Counselor's Handbook. William Campbell

Dog Friendly Gardens, Garden Friendly Dogs. Cheryl Smith

Dog Language, An Encyclopedia of Canine Behavior. Roger Abrantes

Dogs are from Neptune. Jean Donaldson

Evolution of Canine Social Behavior, 2nd ed. Roger Abrantes

From Hoofbeats to Dogsteps. A Life of Listening to and Learning from Animals. Rachel Page Elliott

Get Connected With Your Dog, book with DVD. Brenda Aloff

Give Them a Scalpel and They Will Dissect a Kiss, DVD. Ian Dunbar

Guide to Professional Dog Walking And Home Boarding. Dianne Eibner

Language of Dogs, DVD. Sarah Kalnajs

Mastering Variable Surface Tracking, Component Tracking (2 bk set). Ed Presnall

My Dog Pulls. What Do I Do? Turid Rugaas

New Knowledge of Dog Behavior (reprint). Clarence Pfaffenberger

Oh Behave! Dogs from Pavlov to Premack to Pinker. Jean Donaldson

On Talking Terms with Dogs. Calming Signals, 2nd edition. Turid Rugaas

On Talking Terms with Dogs. What Your Dog Tells You, DVD. Turid Rugaas

Play With Your Dog. Pat Miller

Positive Perspectives. Love Your Dog, Train Your Dog. Pat Miller

Positive Perspectives 2. Know Your Dog, Train Your Dog. Pat Miller

Predation and Family Dogs, DVD. Jean Donaldson

Quick Clicks, 2nd Edition. Mandy Book and Cheryl Smith

Really Reliable Recall. Train Your Dog to Come When Called, DVD. Leslie Nelson

Right on Target. Taking Dog Training to a New Level. Mandy Book & Cheryl Smith
Stress in Dogs. Martina Scholz & Clarissa von Reinhardt
Tales of Two Species. Essays on Loving and Living With Dogs. Patricia McConnell
The Dog Trainer's Resource. The APDT Chronicle of the Dog Collection. Mychelle Blake (*ed*)
The Dog Trainer's Resource 2. The APDT Chronicle of the Dog Collection. Mychelle Blake (*ed*)
The Thinking Dog. Crossover to Clicker Training. Gail Fisher
Therapy Dogs. Training Your Dog To Reach Others. Kathy Diamond Davis
Training Dogs. A Manual (reprint). Konrad Most
Training the Disaster Search Dog. Shirley Hammond
Try Tracking. The Puppy Tracking Primer. Carolyn Krause
Visiting the Dog Park, Having Fun, and Staying Safe. Cheryl S. Smith
When Pigs Fly. Train Your Impossible Dog. Jane Killion
Winning Team. A Guidebook for Junior Showmanship. Gail Haynes
Working Dogs (reprint). Elliot Humphrey & Lucien Warner

HEALTH & ANATOMY, SHOWING
Advanced Canine Reproduction and Whelping. Sylvia Smart
An Eye for a Dog. Illustrated Guide to Judging Purebred Dogs. Robert Cole
Annie On Dogs! Ann Rogers Clark
Another Piece of the Puzzle. Pat Hastings
Canine Cineradiography DVD. Rachel Page Elliott
Canine Massage. A Complete Reference Manual. Jean-Pierre Hourdebaigt
Canine Terminology (reprint). Harold Spira
Breeders Professional Secrets. Ethical Breeding Practices. Sylvia Smart
Dog In Action (reprint). Macdowell Lyon
Dog Show Judging. The Good, the Bad, and the Ugly. Chris Walkowicz
Dogsteps DVD. Rachel Page Elliott
The Healthy Way to Stretch Your Dog. A Physical Therapy Approach. Sasha Foster and Ashley Foster
The History and Management of the Mastiff. Elizabeth Baxter & Pat Hoffman
Performance Dog Nutrition. Optimize Performance With Nutrition. Jocelynn Jacobs
Positive Training for Show Dogs. Building a Relationship for Success Vicki Ronchette
Puppy Intensive Care. A Breeder's Guide To Care Of Newborn Puppies. Myra Savant Harris
Raw Dog Food. Make It Easy for You and Your Dog. Carina MacDonald
Raw Meaty Bones. Tom Lonsdale
Shock to the System. The Facts About Animal Vaccination... Catherine O'Driscoll
Tricks of the Trade. From Best of Intentions to Best in Show, Rev. Ed. Pat Hastings
Work Wonders. Feed Your Dog Raw Meaty Bones. Tom Lonsdale
Whelping Healthy Puppies, DVD. Sylvia Smart

Phone in your Order! 1.800.776.2665 8am-4pm PST / 11am-7pm EST　　　　Sign in | View Cart

Search Dogwise

Everything [▼]　GO

Browse Dogwise

Books & Products
* By Subject
* Dogwise Picks
* Best Sellers
* Best New Titles

Book Reviews
* Find Out How

Resources & Info
* Dogwise Forums
* Dogwise Newsletters
* Dogwise Email List
* Customer Reading Lists
* Dog Show Schedule
* Let Us Know About Your Book or DVD
* Become an Affiliate
* APDT, CPDT
* IAABC
* CAPPDT

Help & Contacts
* About Us
* Contact Us
* Shipping Policy

Employee Picks!
See which books the Dogwise staff members love to read.
* Click Here!

Dog Show Supplies from The 3C's
* Visit the 3c's Website
* View our selection of 3c products.

Save up to 80% on Bargain Books! Click here for Sale, Clearance and hard to find Out of Print titles!
* Click Here!

Prefer to order by phone? Call Us!
1-800-776-2665
8AM - 4PM M-F Pacific Time

Be the First to Hear the News!
Have New Product and Promotion Announcements Emailed to You.
Click Here to Sign Up!

Free Shipping for Orders over $75 - click here for more information!

Win a $25 Dogwise credit - click here to find out how!

Featured New Titles

STRESS IN DOGS - LEARN HOW DOGS SHOW STRESS AND WHAT YOU CAN DO TO HELP, by Martina Scholz & Clarissa von Reinhardt
Item: DTB909
Is stress causing your dog's behavior problems? Research shows that as with humans, many behavioral problems in dogs are stress-related. Learn how to recognize when your dog is stressed, what factors cause stress in dogs, and strategies you can utilize in training and in your daily life with your dog to reduce stress.
Price: $14.95 more information...
DIG IN

SUCCESS IS IN THE PROOFING - A GUIDE FOR CREATIVE AND EFFECTIVE TRAINING, by Debby Quigley & Judy Ramsey
Item: DTO230
The success is indeed in the proofing! Proofing is an essential part of training, but one that is often overlooked or not worked on enough. We all know the story of the dog who can perform a variety of behaviors perfectly in the backyard but falls apart in the obedience ring. This book is full of great ideas and strategies to help your dog do his best no matter what the distractions or conditions may be. Whether competing in Rally or Obedience, trainers everywhere will find this very portable and user friendly book an indispensable addition to their tool box.
Price: $19.95 more information...
DIG IN

REALLY RELIABLE RECALL DVD, by Leslie Nelson
Item: DTB810P
From well-known trainer Leslie Nelson! Easy to follow steps to train your dog to come when it really counts. In an emergency. Extra chapters for difficult to train breeds and training class instructors.
Price: $29.95 more information...
DIG IN

THE DOG TRAINERS RESOURCE - APDT CHRONICLE OF THE DOG COLLECTION, by Mychelle Blake, Editor
Item: DTB880
The modern professional dog trainer needs to develop expertise in a wide variety of fields: learning theory, training techniques, classroom strategies, marketing, community relations, and business development and management. This collection of articles from APDT's Chronicle of the Dog will prove a valuable resource for trainers and would-be trainers.
Price: $24.95 more information...
DIG IN

SHAPING SUCCESS - THE EDUCATION OF AN UNLIKELY CHAMPION, by Susan Garrett
Item: DTA260
Written by one of the world's best dog trainers. Shaping Success gives an excellent explanation of the theory behind animal learning as Susan Garrett trains a high-energy Border Collie puppy to be an agility champion. Buzzy's story both entertains and demonstrates how to apply some of the most up-to-date dog training methods in the real world. Clicker training!
Price: $24.95 more information...
DIG IN

FOR THE LOVE OF A DOG - UNDERSTANDING EMOTION IN YOU AND YOUR BEST FRIEND, by Patricia McConnell
Item: DTB890
Sure to be another bestseller. Trish McConnell's latest book takes a look at canine emotions and body language. Like all her books, this one is written in a way that the average dog owner can follow but brings the latest scientific information that trainers and dog enthusiasts can use.
Price: $24.95 more information...

DIG IN

HELP FOR YOUR FEARFUL DOG: A STEP-BY-STEP GUIDE TO HELPING YOUR DOG CONQUER HIS FEARS, by Nicole Wilde
Item: DTB878
From popular author and trainer Nicole Wilde! A comprehensive guide to the treatment of canine anxiety, fears, and phobias. Chock full of photographs and illustrations and written in a down-to-earth, humorous style.
Price: $24.95 more information...
DIG IN

FAMILY FRIENDLY DOG TRAINING - A SIX WEEK PROGRAM FOR YOU AND YOUR DOG, by Patricia McConnell & Aimee Moore
Item: DTB917
A six-week program to get people and dogs off on the right paw! Includes trouble-shooting tips for what to do when your dog doesn't respond as expected. This is a book that many trainers will want their students to read.
Price: $11.95 more information...

DIG IN

THE LANGUAGE OF DOGS - UNDERSTANDING CANINE BODY LANGUAGE AND OTHER COMMUNICATION SIGNALS DVD SET, by Sarah Kalnajs
Item: DTB875P
Features a presentation and extensive footage of a variety of breeds showing hundreds of examples of canine behavior and body language. Perfect for dog owners or anyone who handles dogs or encounters them regularly while on the job.
Price: $39.95 more information...
DIG IN

THE FAMILY IN DOG BEHAVIOR CONSULTING, by Lynn Hoover
Item: DTB887
Sometimes, no matter how good a trainer or behavior consultant you are, there are issues going on within a human family that you need to be aware of to solve behavior or training problems with dogs. For animal behavior consultants, this text opens up new vistas of challenge and opportunity, dealing with the intense and sometimes complicated nature of relationships between families and dogs.
Price: $24.95 more information...
DIG IN

MORE FROM Dogwise Publishing

WHELPING HEALTHY PUPPIES DVD - Sylvia Smart

AGGRESSION IN DOGS: PRACTICAL MANAGEMENT, PREVENTION & BEHAVIOUR MODIFICATION - Brenda Aloff

PUPPY INTENSIVE CARE: A BREEDER'S GUIDE TO CARE OF NEWBORN PUPPIES - Myra Savant-Harris

TRAINING THE DISASTER SEARCH DOG - Shirley Hammond

GIVE THEM A SCALPEL AND THEY WILL DISSECT A KISS. DOG TRAINING PAST, PRESENT, AND FUTURE DVD - Ian Dunbar

PERFORMANCE DOG NUTRITION: OPTIMIZE PERFORMANCE WITH NUTRITION - Jocelynn Jacobs

PREDATION IN FAMILY DOGS, PREDATION, PREDATORY DRIFT AND PREPAREDNESS SEMINAR DVD - Jean Donaldson

CANINE REPRODUCTION AND WHELPING - A DOG BREEDER'S GUIDE - Myra Savant-Harris

RAW MEATY BONES - Tom Lonsdale

CANINE MASSAGE: A COMPLETE REFERENCE MANUAL - Jean-Pierre Hourdebaigt

DOG LANGUAGE: An ENCYCLOPEDIA OF CANINE BEHAVIOR - Roger Abrantes

MASTERING VARIABLE SURFACE TRACKING BOOK AND WORKBOOK - Ed Presnall

SHOCK TO THE SYSTEM - THE FACTS ABOUT ANIMAL VACCINATION, PET FOOD AND HOW TO KEEP YOUR PETS HEALTHY - Catherine O'Driscoll

THERAPY DOGS: TRAINING YOUR DOG TO REACH OTHERS - Kathy Diamond Davis

TRY TRACKING! THE PUPPY TRACKING PRIMER - Carolyn Krause

WORK WONDERS, FEED YOUR DOG RAW MEATY BONES - Tom Lonsdale

Find out what professional dog trainers from APDT recommend to read and watch!

Click Here for CPDT Reference Books Carried by Dogwise